I Hear and I Forget,

I See and I Remember,

I Do and I Understand.
—Chinese Proverb

It Must be a Bird

Author
Donna VanderWeide

Editor
Betty Cordel

Illustrator
Brenda Wood

Desktop Publisher
Tanya Adams

This book contains materials developed by the AIMS Education Foundation. **AIMS** (**A**ctivities **I**ntegrating **M**athematics and **S**cience) began in 1981 with a grant from the National Science Foundation. The non-profit AIMS Education Foundation publishes hands-on instructional materials (books and the monthly magazine) that integrate curricular disciplines such as mathematics, science, language arts, and social studies. The Foundation sponsors a national program of professional development through which educators may gain both an understanding of the AIMS philosophy and expertise in teaching by integrated, hands-on methods.

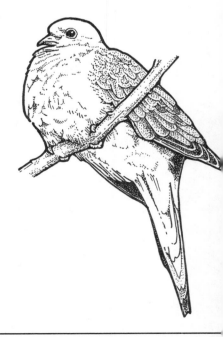

ISBN **1-932093-06-0**
Printed in the United States of America

Table of Contents

It Must be a Bird

In this collection of learning experiences for the young child (Pre-Kindergarten–1st Grade), we will be integrating many aspects of the curriculum and classroom environment to more fully involve the child in applying the science process skills.

Life Science dominates primary science. The appreciation for the natural environment often starts with an interest in birds, which are the most obvious and showy wildlife around us (especially in an urban setting). Children bring many things into the classroom that often fall into this area of study—nests, feathers, eggshells, or eggs found in the neighborhood.

The National Association for the Education of Young Children (NAEYC) advocates a science curriculum that builds on a child's natural environment.

Discovery science is a major part of the curriculum, building on children's natural interest in the world. Science projects are experimental and exploratory and encourage active involvement of every child. The science program takes advantage of natural phenomena such as the outdoors, and the classroom includes many plants and pets for which children provide care daily. Through science projects and field trips, children learn to plan; to dictate and/or write their plans; to apply thinking skills such as hypothesizing, observing, experimenting, and verifying; and many science facts related to their own experience.

from NAEYC as cited in *Doing What Scientists Do* by Ellen Doris (1991), Portsmouth, NH: Heinemann. (pp. 2-3)

In the NAEYC publication *Reaching Potentials: Appropriate Curriculum and Assessment for Young Children* (Vol. 1), edited by Sue Bredekamp and Teresa Rosegrant, a cycle of learning and teaching is defined as meaningful curriculum that is based on an interactive, constructivist view of learning. It begins with **awareness** where teachers create an environment, introduce new objects, invite interest and respond to a child's interest, and enthusiasm. Next the teacher facilitates the child's observations during an **exploration** phase by asking open-ended questions. Then onto **inquiry** where children's interest is guided and focused and more information is provided to help children make connections. Finally, the teacher helps the children apply their learning to new situations in the **utilization** phase.

By using this **naturalist** to **informal** to formal (or **structured**) learning progression, opportunities for observation of the young child enable the teacher to pace the instruction and to provide a "zone of proximal development" (**ZPD**) advocated by Lev Vygotsky. Here a child can be challenged by the teacher or a more mature peer to reach a fuller understanding of scientific concepts.

The **AIMS** *Model of Learning* provides a framework that can be used to facilitate learning. The model suggests that learning occurs in four different ways: real-world experiences; oral and written communication (using language that is abstract); pictorial or graphical communication; and critical thinking.

Throughout this unit of study, students are *doing* things. This entails working in the **circle** environment of real-world experiences. They may be making a model, sorting feathers, or playing a game.

Pictorial or graphical communication represented by the **square** is fulfilled when children graph data and illustrate their experiences. This is a form of communication that migrates across language barriers.

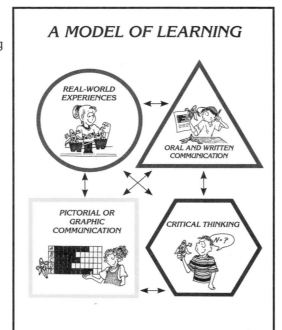

The **triangle** environment of communication is satisfied by students recording results in their journals or by their explaining results to their peers. Abstractions within this environment (writing, reading, and hearing and speaking) take on meaning because of the hands-on experiences in which the children have participated.

The **hexagon** represents the process and products of thinking. Children analyze information, draw conclusions, make generalizations, predict, hypothesize, and construct further tests. Here are represented the critical thinking skills.

This curriculum contains ideas for:
- **Whole Group Activities** —including children's literature and ideas for responding to the literature (including drama, movement, graphing and creative writing).
- **Small Group and Paired Activities**—task cards for games, art, book-making and math activities.
- **PLUS: Music, Poetry and Cooking**—learning experiences to touch all learning styles and abilities.

These learning explorations are planned around three documents:
- *Benchmarks for Science Literacy, Project 2061*
  American Association for the Advancement of Science
  Oxford University Press, New York, 1993.
- *Principles and Standards for School Mathematics*
  National Council of Teachers of Mathematics
  Reston, VA, 2000.
- *National Science Education Standards*
  National Research Council
  National Academy Press, Washington, DC, 1996.

As well as *Reaching Potentials: Appropriate Curriculum and Assessment for Young Children (Vol.1)*
  National Association for the Education of Young Children
  Editors: Sue Bredekamp and Teresa Rosegrant
  Washington, DC.

Guiding Documents

Project 2061 Benchmarks

Children should have lots of time to talk about what they observe and to compare their observations with those of others.

- People can often learn about things around them by just observing those things carefully, but sometimes they can learn more by doing something to the things and noting what happens.
- Tools such as thermometers, magnifiers, rulers or balances often give more information about things than can be obtained by just observing things without their help.
- Describing things as accurately as possible is important in science because it enables people to compare their observations with those of others.
- When people give different descriptions of the same thing, it is usually a good idea to make some fresh observations instead of just arguing about who is right. (p. 10)

Science should begin in kindergarten with students learning to work in small teams (rather than as isolated individuals) to ask and answer questions about their surroundings and to share their findings with classmates. ...Given the value that science places on independent thought, it is important that students be assured that although they are part of a team, they are free to reach different conclusions from their classmates, and that when they do, they should say so and say why.

- Everybody can do science and invent things and ideas.
- In doing science, it is often helpful to work with a team and to share findings with others. All team members should reach their own individual conclusions, however, about what the findings mean.
- A lot can be learned about plants and animals by observing them closely, but care must be taken to know the needs of living things and how to provide for them in the classroom. (p. 15)

National Science Education Standards

During the elementary grades, children build understanding of biological concepts through direct experience with living things, their life cycles, and their habitats. (p. 127)

NCTM Standards 2000*

Sharing gives students opportunities to hear new ideas and compare them with their own and to justify their thinking. As students struggle with problems, seeing a variety of successful solutions improves their chance of learning useful strategies and allows them to determine if some strategies are more flexible and efficient. (pp. 118-119)

Language, whether used to express ideas or to receive them, is a very powerful tool and should be used to foster the learning of mathematics. Communicating about mathematical ideas is a way for students to articulate, clarify, organize, and consolidate their thinking. Students, like adults, exchange thoughts and ideas in many ways—orally; with gestures; and with pictures, objects, and symbols. By listening carefully to others, students can become aware of alternative perspectives and strategies. (p. 128)

* Reprinted with permission from *Principles and Standards for School Mathematics,* 2000 by the National Council of Teachers of Mathematics. All rights reserved.

Conceptual Focus

Covering
Feathers
- All birds have feathers. They vary in size, color, and uses.
- Many birds fly but some do not.
- Birds molt or shed feathers on a regular basis to get rid of worn or damaged feathers.
- Some birds fly (migrate) to other locations during certain seasons of the year.
- The vane of a bird's feather is hollow which keeps it lightweight, an adaptation essential to bird flight.
- Birds are the fastest moving animals. Some can fly over 100 miles per hour.
- Feathers keep the bird warm in the winter and ventilated in the summer.
- Feathers help to camouflage the bird.

Physical Characteristics
Beaks
- Birds eat different things. Some of them eat seeds. Some eat fruit. Some eat fish or meat.
- Birds beaks give clues as to what things they eat. Different types of beaks include:
  - Spearing—herons or egrets
  - Cracking—finches, sparrows, grosbeaks
  - Straining—flamingos
  - Chisel—woodpeckers
  - Spoon—ducks and spoonbills
  - Probing—creepers

Feet
- All birds have two feet. They vary in size, number of toes, shapes, and uses. Bird's feet give clues about where they live and what they eat. Different types of feet include:
  - Swimming—loons, ducks
  - Perching (three toes forward, one back)—songbirds
  - Wading—shorebirds, herons, egrets
  - Climbing (two toes forward, two back)—woodpecker, nuthatches
  - Grasping—(birds of prey), eagles, hawks, owl

Size and Shape
- Birds come in different sizes and shapes.
- Different kinds of birds live in different parts of the world in different climates.

Bones
- All birds have hollow bones.
- All birds have backbones.

Warm-Blooded
- All birds are warm-blooded.

Habitat and Reproduction
Eggs
- **All birds lay eggs.** Eggs differ in size, shapes, coloration and gestation period. Some birds lay eggs in other bird's nests.

Diet
- **Birds eat different things.** Some of them eat seeds. Some eat fruit. Some eat fish or meat.

General Philosophy of Early Years Learning

For the young child, the learning center, task card approach works well to support the levels of development from concrete to abstract. Peer tutoring encourages verbalization and communication. The teacher becomes facilitator, enabler, and conductor where problem solving involves many of the science process skills:

1. **Observation**—utilizes the five senses to gather information to be processed

2. **Comparing and contrasting**—likenesses and differences are noted

3. **Classification**—various properties are grouped and sorted

4. **Measuring**—observations are quantified and seriation is used for organizing materials

5. **Communication**—children talk about, illustrate, and write down their discoveries and observations so that others are informed while encouraging the child to organize data

6. **Inferring**—with this information now part of their knowledge base, children can draw conclusions about what they can **expect** to happen and what **would** happen if certain circumstances occurred.

Throughout this approach, **curiosity** is encouraged and concept instruction is facilitated through **problem solving**.

In an early childhood classroom, a thorough integration of the different academic areas and creative aspects of play and work more fully utilizes the haptic nature of the young child. Small group and total group time is kept to a minimum and best utilized for mini lessons on specific concepts or for general informational input by teachers or observations by the children.

Balance is the key. The environment is one of the best teachers in a young child's classroom; therefore, our emphasis in this unit of study will be ways to set-up the learning experiences for full child engagement. We know firsthand experiences are essential for learning. We want to enhance our student's awareness by creating situations where they need to observe, and then share these observations through visual depiction, drawing, and/or discussion. We know the teacher will be guiding these observations by supplying correct vocabulary terms and asking open-ended divergent questions to heighten the child's awareness. A risk-free environment will encourage differences of opinions and stimulate interest and promote further discussion. Teachers of young children are always mindful that misconceptions are part of the learning process. They will give explicit instruction where necessary.

Finally, teachers recognize that different abilities, learning modalities, and cultures exist in every classroom. By providing many approaches to learning and assessing knowledge, every child can be a successful learner and scientist.

The Young Child's Environment

Library
Provide related bird books (content-factual)

Science/Exploration Center
In science center have tripod magnifier set up with bird pictures, nests, feathers, eggs ... (whatever is brought in).

Art Center
a) Provide paints for bird pictures; b) Add feathers to collage box

Language Center
a) Provide blank books for drawing and writing words about birds; b) Display copies of poetry and songs for this unit; c) Word banks that children generate. Add to these regularly.

Game Center
a) Provide a labeled bird outline over which students can lay tissue paper squares for tracing and writing labels of parts. Tissue paper can be held in place with clothespins (see *Resources);* b) Environment cards (see *Resources*); c) Word Bingo with bird names; d) Bird Dominoes; e) Silhouettes and bird match-ups (see *Silhouette Matching*); f) Language boards with birds.

Homemaking Center
Provide binoculars and a camera in a bag for "bird watchers." Include pad and pencil for sketching what you find!

Block Center
Provide a) small bowls for "nests" and encourage tree building or environment creation; b) blue cellophane squares for water fowl; c) small sticks for eagles' nests; d) small toy trees and "bird houses" from Tinker Toys™.

Drama Center
Bird puppets; beak noses (on elastic); prop boxes for: veterinarian's office, pet store, zoo

Sand or Water Table
Set up for different habitats

Math
Provide a) balance; b) Unifix cubes; c) Geoboards and bands; d) paper and pencil for drawing and writing about observations.

Listening Center
Provide books and tape sets and tape recorder for reading and re-reading of bird books.

Music
a) Provide posters of songs and poems from this unit of study. Have available "Read the Wall" tools for re-reading, singing or chanting. ("Read the Wall" tools include glasses with frames only, flyswatter with window cut out, pointer, flashlight, and so on.); b) Bird songs tapes or CD's; c) Xylophones for matching bird songs **or** playing songs from book **or** creating new songs.

Room Displays

- Have bird pictures mounted and labeled with bird's name. Sources: Nature magazines like: *Ranger Rick, In Your Backyard, Texas Highways, Arizona Highways*. See *Resources* for charts. Check with your local Audubon chapter.

- Create a habitat mural on your wall. Include a tree using paper raffia for trunk and large craft paper for leaves, a pond, a mountain side, etc. (Whatever your natural area provides for bird habitats).

- Encourage children to create birds for the habitats you've provided. These may be two- or three-dimensional. Collage boxes and the children's easel paintings will provide the necessary materials. Refer children to the bird pictures you've provided. Encourage the observation of number of eyes, legs, wings, etc.

Using the Songs

The following suggestions offer a five-step process for utilizing the songs in this book.

Suggestions

1. Enlarge the pages in this book for whole group read-alongs.

2. After several whole group readings, use child-sized books for individual read-alongs. With these, children can "track and touch" words they are already familiar with from their whole group, large book experiences. This is done with the teacher in small groups (6–8 children) so that the teacher can watch for left to right, top to bottom, "zip back to the beginning of the next row," reading conventions. **It's imperative that each child "say and touch" the corresponding words on their personal reading page.** The neural imprinting of say-touch-look creates a sense of word-ness.

3. Each child then independently illustrates each section. This will require re-reading by the child. Have the children use pencils **only**. This will encourage detailed illustrations without obscuring their drawings with color.

4. When through illustrating, the child can share text and pictures with the teacher (or a friend) for another re-telling of text.

5. Parent involvement is assured as this illustrated personal book goes home and becomes part of the child's at-home library.

Beaks
(Tune: "Ants Go Marching")
—by Donna VanderWeide

(Have corresponding pictures for each bird. Allow children to make up motions to go with each beak.)

My beak is short and strong, I go chomp, chomp—chomp, chomp.
My beak is short and strong, I go chomp, chomp—chomp, chomp.
My beak is short and strong, indeed.
It's perfect to break open seeds
And I like to fly around, to look, for seeds all day.
(Grosbeak, sparrow, finch, cardinal)

Grosbeak

My beak is long and flat, I go splash, splash—splash, splash.
My beak is long and flat, I go splash, splash—splash, splash.
My beak is long and flat. I need
To scoop up fish from out of the sea,
And I separate the fish, from weeds, to get the food I need.
(Spoonbills and pelicans)

Spoonbill

Heron

My beak is long and very sharp—stab, stab—stab, stab.
My beak is long and very sharp—stab, stab—stab, stab.
My beak is long and sharp, it's true.
I'm after fish and frogs for food,
And I wade in water, slow, to fool, the fish I eat.
(Heron)

Introductory Activity
To access prior knowledge about birds

Topic
Birds

Key Question
What do we know about birds?

Focus
Students will draw on prior knowledge to contribute to group discussion.

Guiding Documents
Project 2061 Benchmarks
Natural phenomena easily capture the attention of these youngsters, but they should be encouraged to wonder about mathematical technological phenomena as well. Questions about numbers, shapes and artifacts, for example, should be treated with the same interest as those about rocks and birds. ...As students learn to write, they should start keeping a class list of things they wonder about, without regard to how easy it might be to answer their own questions. Teachers should then help them learn to pick from the list the questions they can find answers to by doing something such as collecting, sorting, counting, drawing, taking something apart, or making something. At this level, questions that can be answered descriptively are to be preferred over those requiring abstract explanations. Students are more likely to come up with reasonable answers as to "how" and "what" than as to "why." (p. 285)

NRC Standards
Abilities necessary to do scientific inquiry
- *Ask a question about objects, organisms, and events in the environment.*
- *Employ simple equipment and tools to gather data and extend the senses.*

Science
Life science
  characteristics of organisms
  organisms and environments

Integrated Processes
Observing
Communicating

Materials
Large writing surface (poster board or butcher wrap)
Permanent pens of different colors
Masking tape
White paper, 8.5" x 11" cut in half, one per student
Sticky notes

Procedure (Total Group Activity—Teacher led)
1. Prepare a KWL chart on large sheet of butcher wrap.

	What do we think we know? K	What do we want to know? W	What have we learned? L
How birds look			
What they eat			
Where they live			
?			

2. Ask students to close their eyes and picture a bird. "Look at its colors. Look at its body. Look at its face. Look at its feet. Look at its size. Now open your eyes."
3. "Tell me what you saw in your mind."
4. Fill in the *K* section with a different-colored pen for each idea and a quick sketch of that idea. (This aids eye tracking and delineates the different ideas.) Guide discussion to generate ideas about how birds eat, live, look, etc. Ask children to decide into which section to put their ideas. Random ideas are included in *?* section.
5. Ask children to illustrate their bird on half of an 8.5" x 11" piece of paper. Use these pictures as a pre-assessment. (These may be dated for the child's portfolio. At the end of the study, they will do this again for comparison of growth of knowledge.)
6. For children that are writing, encourage the addition of words or letters. For other students, scribe the description the child gives.
7. Create separate posters of "How they look," "What they eat," "Where they live" for the language center so that children can use terms to create a frame sentence.
8. Ask children what they want to learn about birds. Put each question on a sticky note with the child's name on it. Attach to a chart area *What do we want to know?*
9. Fill in *What have we learned?* during and at the end of study.

Home Link
Send home the note to parents asking for their participation in the study of birds.

Dear Parents:

We are beginning a Life Science study of **Birds**.

We would like to ask you to send to school any books, feathers, nests (empty!) or clean egg shells you may have at home. If you or a friend has a bird as a pet and would be willing to let the bird spend a short time with us, we would be very grateful.

We will be making bird feeders to encourage birds to come into your yard for closer observation. Start now to draw your child's attention to birds as you notice them in your neighborhood. (What are they eating? How are they moving from place to place? Where do they live? Do they make a noise or have a song?) Encourage your child to draw the birds they see.

Thank you for your help.

Sincerely,

- -

Return to school

☐ Yes, I have a bird to share for a day!

It's a _____.

_____   _____
Parent's Name   Telephone Number

It Must Be a Bird

Tune: "Must Be Santa"

—by Donna VanderWeide

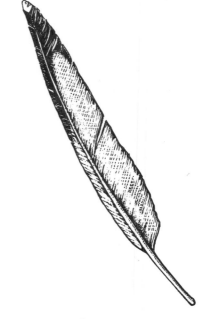

Who's got feathers everywhere?
    Birds have feather everywhere.
Who's got wings that try to fly?
    Birds have wings that try to fly.
Feathers here, try to fly.
      It's got feathers (3x's)
      It must be a bird.

Who's got feet to perch and climb?
    Birds have feet to perch and climb.
Who's got legs with scales and claws?
    Birds have legs with scales and claws.
Scales and claws, perch and climb, feathers here try to fly
      It's got feathers (3x's)
      It must be a bird.

Who's got a tail that moves to steer?
    Birds have tails that move to steer.
Who's got eyes on the side of its head?
    Birds have eyes on the sides of their heads.
Eyes on side, tails to steer, scales and claws,
perch and climb, feathers here try to fly.
      It's got feathers (3x's)
      It must be a bird.

Feathers

Background Information

Birds are the only creatures that are covered by feathers. There are three main types of feathers:

Down Feathers—fluffy ones that are next to the birds' skin to keep it warm

Body Feathers—long and smooth that give the bird its color, shape, and pattern

Flight Feathers—long and stiff ones that are part of the bird's wing or tail

Feathers have a central shaft that contains air pockets to make the feather lighter and to aid the bird in flight. Barbs extend from the shaft and are held together with barbules that hook together like a zipper. Birds use their beaks to align these barbs in a process called preening.

Each feather is attached to a muscle that the bird can maneuver. Waterfowl have oil glands under the skin and use their bills to not only separate the feathers but to spread the oil over the feathers to make them more waterproof.

All feathers are lightweight, warm, and waterproof. As feathers wear out, they fall out in a process called molting. Ducks molt all at once and so are unable to fly for a few weeks while new feathers grow back in. (See *Make Way for Ducklings* by Robert McClosky.)

The numbers of feathers vary with the size and habitat of the bird. The ruby-throated hummingbird has 1500 feathers; the bald eagle has more than 7000; the mallard duck has 12,000 feathers that keep it warm in cold water; the tundra swan has 25,000 feathers. Sizes of feathers vary from the tiny bee hummingbird (of Cuba) to the ostrich and peacock.

Even though they all have feathers, not all birds can fly. The penguin's wings are especially adapted to swimming. The ostrich doesn't fly, it runs to escape its enemies. Rheas are able to run faster than a horse (31 mph) and are good swimmers.

Flight provides birds a means of obtaining food and/or escaping danger. Most birds fly by flapping their wings up and down. As they push down, the air moves back, and they move forward. The curved wings provide lift as the airflow over the top of the curved wings moves faster than the air below the wing. One-third of the eagle's weight is in its wings while the hummingbird's wing is only one-twentieth of its weight.

Wing shapes vary from long and wide for soaring birds (vultures and hawks) that ride thermal air currents to long and narrow wings for gliding birds (the albatross). Short and fast birds (the pheasant) have wide and rounded wing shapes, while other fast flyers (the swallow) have narrow and pointed wings.

Wing feathers may be adapted for special uses such as the long rides of the albatross which can glide on the air currents for long periods of time. Falcons can dive at 150 miles per hour with their special long, narrow wing feathers.

Other unusual feather uses include the grouse that splashes water on its fine down feathers to feed its baby. Turkey vultures have no feathers on their head or neck to mess up when eating carrion (dead animals).

Feathers vary in their overall appearance and size and provide the color of the bird's wings, breast, back, undertail, and legs. The colors vary with the sex, age, season, and diet. Bird patterns vary on the face, wings, and tails and give each type of bird its special appearance.

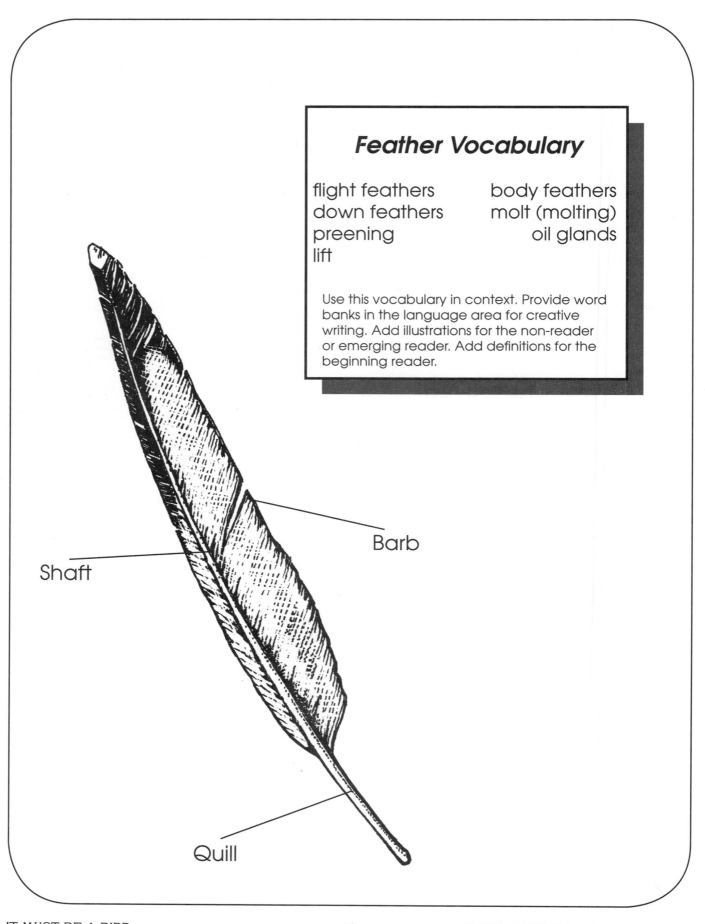

Feather Vocabulary

flight feathers   body feathers
down feathers   molt (molting)
preening   oil glands
lift

Use this vocabulary in context. Provide word banks in the language area for creative writing. Add illustrations for the non-reader or emerging reader. Add definitions for the beginning reader.

Barb

Shaft

Quill

Large Group—Book
Feathers for Lunch
—by Lois Ehlert

Skills
Predicting
Observing
Listening
Reader's Theater

Procedure
Part One
Show cover of book *Feathers for Lunch* and ask children to tell what they think this book is about. List these guesses on a chart using a different-colored pen for each guess.

Part Two
Tell the children you will read the book twice. "The first time we'll enjoy the story and pictures. The second time we'll stop to talk about what you've noticed that is special about this book and we'll check your guesses."

Part Three
On the second reading, stop before you say the rhyming word and let children supply word. Check their guesses. Identify birds and plants if students are unable.

Part Four
Use bird pictures to play "Bird, Bird, what do you see?" (similar to "Brown Bear, Brown Bear … ").

Class chants: *"Robin, Robin, who do you see?"*
"Robin" answers: *"I see Blue Jay looking at me."*
Class chants: *"Blue Jay, Blue Jay, who do you see?"*
"Blue Jay" answers: *"I see… ."*
Last bird says, *"I see that cat chasing me,"* "and me," "and me" says each bird in turn back to the "Robin."
Say all together: *"Let's fly away!"*
Then "fly" to a friend and give them a card.
See if children can arrange themselves in the same order.

Extensions
1. Make two sets of the *Environment Cards* (24 total) from the *Resource* section for the Memory Game. Color and laminate. As a paired activity, place cards face down on the floor. The first child will turn over two cards trying to find two that match. If a match is made, the child takes the pair of cards and turns over two more cards trying to find another match. This child continues to play until he or she does not make a match. When no match is made, the two cards are turned face down again and the play goes to the second child. The child with the most matches wins.
2. Make two sets of *Environment Cards* for Environment Match. Color and laminate. Cut the names of the birds off the cards. Turn name cards and bird picture cards face down on the floor. Children will play in the same fashion as Memory Game, but this time they will match the picture of the bird with its name.
3. Put one set of the small cards (12 total) face down on the floor. Have one child pick up a card and describe the bird to a friend. The friend tries to name the bird that has been described. Have children switch roles.

Song
Feathers for Lunch
(tune: "Farmer in the Dell")
by Donna VanderWeide

(Use with 8.5" x 11" cards. Add speech balloons with song of birds.)

The cat chased the _____ (bird)
The cat chased the _____ (bird)
The ____(bird) said, "____, ____, _____,
And then flew away.

American Robin

Blue Jay

Cardinal

House Wren

Woodpecker

Red–winged Blackbird

Oriole

Mourning Dove

Northern Flicker

Hummingbird

Sparrow

Goldfinch

25

Tell Me a Story
Feathers for Lunch
—by Lois Ehlert

Suggestions for use:
Use these cards to help the children retell the story.

Run the pictures on card stock. Try using watercolors to color the cards. This allows you to shade the pictures and make the illustrations more like those in the book. Laminate to preserve the cards.

You may write the text of the story on the back of the cards for you or the children to read as they retell the story.

The cards can be placed on the chalkboard tray or on the floor or on a clothesline strung between two chairs. This last method works well in centers where two children can work together—one reading the story from the book and the other using clothespins to place the pictures on the line as they occur in the story.

The pictures can also work as cue cards as the children act out the story or make a variation with different settings or birds. Let the children make their own cards.

You may want to add "speech balloons" to each picture with the bird's sound.

Feather Task Cards

Topic
Properties of feathers

Key Question
How do we sort and group feathers?

Focus
The students will note similarities and differences in feathers and group them accordingly.

Guiding Documents
Project 2061 Benchmarks
- *People can often learn about things around them by just observing those things carefully, but sometimes they can learn more by doing something to the things and noting what happens.*
- *Tools such as thermometers, magnifiers, rulers or balances often give more information about things than can be obtained by just observing things without their help.*
- *Describing things as accurately as possible is important in science because it enables people to compare their observations with those of others.*
- *When people give different descriptions of the same thing, it is usually a good idea to make some fresh observations instead of just arguing about who is right.*
- *Tools are used to do things better or more easily and to do some things that could not otherwise be done at all. In technology, tools are used to observe, measure, and make things.*
- *When trying to build something or to get something to work better, it usually helps to follow directions if there are any or to ask someone who has done it before for suggestions.*
- *People are more likely to believe your ideas if you can give good reasons for them.*
- *Describe and compare things in terms of number, shape, texture, size, weight, color, and motion.*
- *Draw pictures that correctly portray at least some features of the thing being described.*

NRC Standards
- *Scientists use different kinds of investigations depending on the questions they are trying to answer. Types of investigations include describing objects, events, and organisms; classifying them; and doing a fair test (experimenting).*
- *Simple instruments, such as magnifiers, thermometers, and rulers, provide more information than scientists obtain using only their senses.*
- *Organisms have basic needs. For example, animals need air, water, and food; plants require air, water, nutrients, and light. Organisms can survive only in environments in which their needs can be met. The world has many different environments and distinct environments support the life of different types of organisms.*
- *Each plant or animal has different structures that serve different functions in growth, survival, and reproduction. For example, humans have distinct body structures for walking, holding, seeing, and talking.*

NCTM Standards 2000*

- *Count with understanding and recognize "how many" in sets of objects*
- *Connect number words and numerals to the quantities they represent, using various models and representation.*
- *Recognize the attributes of length, volume, weight, area, and time*
- *Compare and order objects according to these attributes*
- *Understand how to measure using nonstandard and standard units*
- *Recognize, name, build, draw, compare, and sort two- and three-dimensional shapes*

Science

Life science
    characteristics of organisms
    organisms and environments

Math

Measuring
    mass
    length
Graphing
Counting

Integrated Processes

Observing
Comparing and contrasting
Communicating
Sorting and classifying

Materials

Feathers, assorted
Hand lenses or tripod magnifier
Balance
Eyedropper
Water container
Large zippers, mounted
Trays
Poster board
Paper plates
Craft sticks
Adding machine tape
Wallpaper sample books
Hole punch
Shoelaces
Student journals
Unifix cubes
Paper clips
5" x 7" index cards
Styrofoam meat trays
AIMS Grouping Circles
Ink
Ribbon
Tempera paint
Task Cards for learning stations (see *Management*)

Management

1. You may
   - Run the task cards on colored card stock to code them for different tasks (e.g., all *feather* experiences one color or all *math* same color). Laminate so that the student side can be displayed in learning stations; *or*
   - Duplicate and mount on a file folder or a large index card. (Student directions on one side and teacher directions on the other.) Color and laminate.
2. Introduce one *Task Card* at a time.
3. Model the directions printed on the card.
4. If there is a drawing or written response expected, model that also. Leave your model at the learning station for children to reference.
5. If interest remains high in a station, leave it for the children when you add the next station. Stations may be set up on a special table or on a cookie sheet or serving tray placed in an out-of-the-way area in your classroom, preferably near a window.
6. Note: In the set of *Task Cards,* there are *Teacher Resource Cards* that do not have an accompanying *Student Card.* These consist of centers or games that you can set up for the children and only require verbal directions from the teacher.

* Reprinted with permission from *Principles and Standards for School Mathematics,* 2000 by the National Council of Teachers of Mathematics. All rights reserved.

Feather Feelers

Skills
Observing
Comparing and contrasting
Describing words
Sorting and classifying
Ordering

Materials
3 paper plates
Assorted feathers
Cardboard pieces

Directions
1. Attach various flight feathers to stiff cardboard pieces (one feather per piece).
2. Have students sort/classify the feathers on the paper plates.
3. Ask the students to order the feather from shortest to longest.

Extension
Write a descriptive phrase of a feather on the chalkboard by taking a child's dictation.

Feathers —Mathematics, Literary Link • Activity 1—Teacher Card

---

Feather Feelers

Directions: You may sort by color or by size. Tell a friend why you chose to sort the feathers this way.

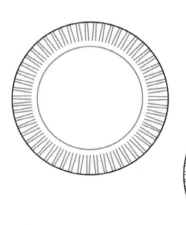 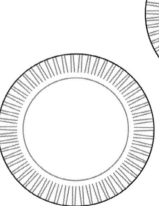 

Take any six feathers and line them up from the shortest to longest feather.

Feathers • Activity 1—Student Card

What's My Rule?

Skills
Observing
Comparing and contrasting
Sharing
Thinking
Describing

Materials
Large tray
Paper plate
Assorted feathers
Student journal

Directions
1. Tape a paper plate to the middle of the tray.
2. Scatter feathers on tray around the plate.
3. Model for the children how to choose a group of feathers and place them on the plate (e.g., all one color).
4. Ask them to identify your rule.
5. Have students draw a picture of their rule and write words to describe the rule.
6. Return the feathers to the tray.
7. Have students do the same procedure.

Feathers—Mathematics • Activity 2—Teacher Card

What's My Rule?

Directions
- Place loose feathers on tray.
- Decide with your friend which feathers are alike in some way.
- Place those feathers on the plate.
- In your journal, draw the feather rule you chose.

- Write the words that describe your feathers.
- Now return feathers to the tray and choose a different rule.
- Add that picture and rule to your journal.
- Do at least four rules.

Feathers • Activity 2—Student Card

Graph a Handful of Feathers

Skills
Observing
Comparing and contrasting
Graphing
Counting

Materials
Bag of feathers
Crayons
Poster board
Duplicates of chart

Directions
- Enlarge the graph onto poster board and laminate.
- Have students graph a handful of feathers according to graph's descriptors.
- Have students compare and contrast their results with others.

Number

4
3
2
1

one color   two colors   pattern

Feathers—Game, Mathematics, Science • Activity 3—Teacher Card

Graph a Handful of Feathers

Directions
- Take a handful of feathers.
- Place each feather on the graph.
- Tell which one had the most, the least, the same.
- Try with another handful.
- Compare your results.

Complete this sentence:

I can hold _____ feathers in one hand.

Feathers • Activity 3—Student Card

Create a Bird

Skill
Observing patterns

Materials
Construction paper
Feathers
Markers, pencils, art chalk

Directions
- Glue a feather to a sheet of construction paper.
- Provide markers, crayons, colored pencils, art chalk.
- Have students create a bird around the feather maintaining the colors and/or patterns of the feather.

Feathers—Art, Mathematics • Activity 4—Teacher Card

Create a Bird

Directions
- Draw a bird around the feather.
- Add the same colors and/or patterns you see on the feather.

Feathers • Activity 4—Student Card

Snappy Feathers

Skills
Observing
Comparing and contrasting
Measuring
Counting
Writing numbers
Using tools
Comparative vocabulary

Materials
Unifix cubes
Bag of feathers
Paper (or journal)
Pencil

Directions
- Place materials on a tray and model activity for children. (See directions on *Student Card.*)

Extensions
1. If appropriate, continue with:

   My longer feather has _____ more cubes than my shorter feather.

   My shorter feather has _____ fewer cubes than the longer feather.

   If I placed the two cube trains together, I would have _____ cubes.

   For younger child, have them tell a friend or a teacher about their numbers.

2. Use 1" grid paper to draw around feathers, to estimate area, perimeter, and write comparative terms about findings.

Snappy Feathers

Directions
- Choose two feathers from the bag.
- Place the feathers on the paper and draw around each feather with a pencil.
- Snap Unifix cubes together until the train is same length as the longer feather.
- Do the same for the shorter feather.
- Count the cubes for each feather.
- Write how long each feather is.

Write these sentences on your paper:

My longer feather is _____ cubes long.

My shorter feather is _____ cubes long.

Drip - Drop Flyers

Skills
Observing
Using science tools
Communicating

Materials
2 eyedroppers
Flight and down feathers
Cup of water
Paper or journal
Pencil
Oil
Cotton ball
Pictures of water fowl

Background Information
To waterproof and keep feathers in good shape, birds spread oil on feathers from a special preen gland on the base of the tail.

Grouse use downy feathers to channel water to their babies.

Directions
• Have pictures of different water fowl displayed at this center.
• Ask students to name a bird that needs feathers that do not hold water. (e.g., duck)
• Go through the activity with the students.

Extension
Place feathers on the surface of some water. Do they sink or float? Add oil to feathers and repeat eyedropper experiment. What do you notice?

Feathers—Science Tools • Activity 6—Teacher Card

Drip - Drop Flyers

• Use eyedropper to drop water on a feather.
   What shape does the drop take?
   What happens to the feather as you drop more water on it?
• Use a **flight** feather and a **down** feather.
   What differences do you notice about the feathers when you drop water on them?
• Shake each feather.
   What happens to the water?
   Which feather held onto the water better?
• Draw a picture of what you've done and write (or tell) someone about your experience.

Feathers • Activity—Student Card

© 2004 AIMS Education Foundation

A Pan of Feathers

Skills
Observing
Comparing and contrasting
Finding mass
Using science tools

Materials
Assorted feathers
Unifix cubes
Balance
Journal or paper
Pencil

Directions
• Add feathers to one pan of the balance.
• Add Unifix cubes to the other pan until the pans equalize.

Extension
Have children determine what other things they could use in second cup to which to compare the mass of the feathers. (e.g., paper clips, pencils, crayons)

Feathers—Mathematics, Science Tools • Activity 7—Teacher Card

A Pan of Feathers

• Fill one pan with feathers.
• Draw a pan on your paper.
• Write how many Unifix cubes you think it will take to balance the pan of feathers.
• Now drop one cube at a time into the other pan until it balances.
• Write that number on your picture.
• Compare your numbers.

Feathers • Activity 7—Student Card

Light as a Feather

Skills
Observing
Comparing and contrasting

Materials
Flight feathers
Journal or paper
Pencil

Background Information
Feathers are hollow and light so that birds can fly.

Directions
- Have students determine the number of twists and turns a feather makes after it is dropped.
- Direct them to compare this number with the number of twists and turns the feather makes when dropped from a higher point.

Feathers—Science, Movement • Activity 8—Teacher Card

Light as a Feather

- Hold the feather on your hand.
- Blow it away.
  What happens?
- Working with a friend, count the turns before it hits the ground.
- Draw what you see.
- Write the number of turns.
- Stand on a chair. Predict what will happen now that the feather will fall from a higher point.
- Drop the feather and count the turns.
- Write that number down.
  What do you notice?

Become a feather. Let your friend "blow" on you. How would you fall to the ground?

Feathers • Activity 8—Student Card

Feathers Have Zippers

Skills
Using science tools
Observing
Comparing

Materials
Flight feathers
Hand lens or tripod magnifier
Paper or journal
Pencil

Background Information
Flight feathers have a flat blade (vane) which joins to the central rod (shaft). The tip is called the quill. The feather has no living material so if it is damaged, it cannot heal. However, the feathers can be hooked and unhooked by separating their barbs. Birds care for their feathers by using their beaks in a process called preening.

Feathers Have Zippers

Use a feather to try to:
- Ruffle it —
  Pull the feather with one finger from top to bottom.
  Draw what your feather looks like.

- Mend it —
  Pull your finger and thumb along the feather from bottom to top.
  Draw your feather now.

Check it out with a hand lens.
  What do you see when you ruffle?
  What do you see when you mend it?

Feathers • Activity 9—Student Card

Feathers Have Zippers
(Tune: "Zippity Doo Dah")
—by Donna VanderWeide

Feathers have zippers.
Feathers have barbs.
Pull them apart and they
won't go far.

Birds use their beaks
And zip them back up.
Feathers have zippers.
Feathers have barbs.

Feather Sayings
To Illustrate

Skill
Creative thinking

Materials
Cards
Pencil
Paper

Directions
- Write each saying on a separate 5" x 7" index card and laminate.
  Light as a feather
  Feather your nest
  Knock me over with a feather
  A feather in your cap
  Birds of a feather flock together
  Fly the coop
  Travel as the crow flies
- Instruct students to illustrate the feather sayings.

Extension
Have student do two illustrations: one illustration of what that saying means, the other illustration of the saying with something other than a feather. (e.g., *Knock me over with a* boxing glove.)

Feathers—Literary Link • Activity 10—Teacher Card

- -

Feather Sayings
To Illustrate

Choose a saying and draw a picture of it. Write (or dictate) what you think this saying means.

- *Light as a feather*
- *Feather your nest*
- *Knock me over with a feather*
- *A feather in your cap*
- *Birds of a feather flock together*
- *Fly the coop*
- *Travel as the crow flies*

Feathers • Activity 10—Student Card

Hummingbird Helicopters

Skills
Observing
Measuring
Counting

Materials
Hummingbird pattern
Scissors
Adding machine tape
Crayons
Small paper clips

Directions
- Provide pattern for children to color and decorate like a hummingbird.
- Have students cut along solid outlines.
- Tell them to fold the side flaps to the back along the dashed line.
- Have students fold one wing forward and one wing backward.
- Give students a paper clip to attach to the bottom of the hummingbird.
- Have students drop the hummingbird and count the number of circles it makes until it lands on the floor.
- Invite the students to vary the height of the drop.
- Chart the numbers.

Feathers—Art, Mathematics • Activity 11—Teacher Card

Hummingbird Helicopters

- Have your friend cut a piece of adding machine tape as tall as you are and tape it to the wall. Drop the "hummingbird" from that height and count how many circles the "hummingbird" makes until it lands on the floor.
- Write that number on the adding machine tape.
- Now stand on a chair and have your friend cut another piece of adding machine tape as tall as you are while on the chair.

- Predict how the height will affect the number of turns.
- Drop the "hummingbird" from this new height and count how many circles the "hummingbird" makes until it lands on the floor.
- Write that number on the adding machine tape.
- Compare the numbers.
- Switch roles.

Feathers • Activity 11—Student Card

Hummingbird Helicopters

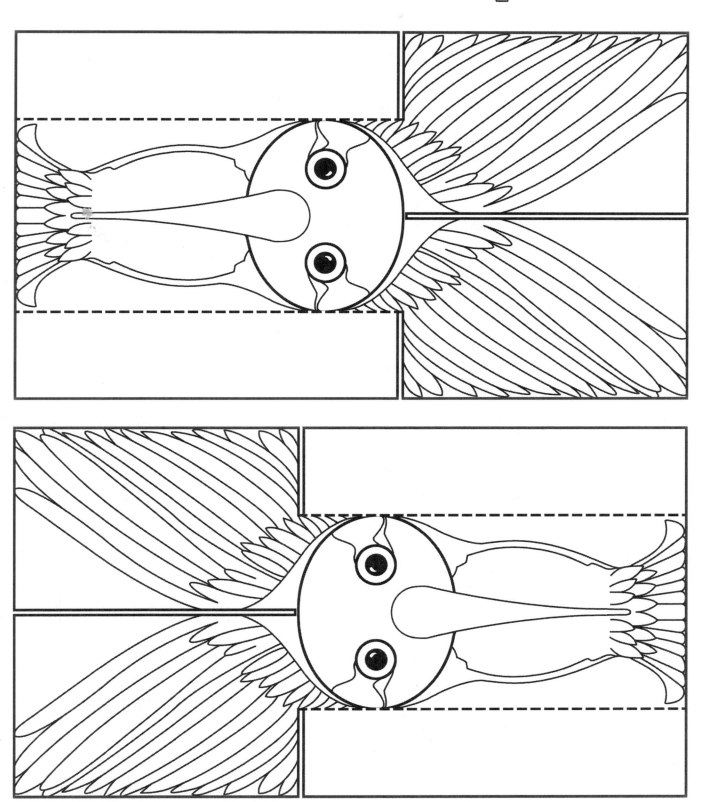

Feather in Your Hat

Skills
Observing
Patterns
Number relationships and order
Communicating mathematically

Materials
2 3-inch wide strips of corrugated cardboard, cut long
enough to fit the circumference of a child's head
Assorted flight feathers, stiff and long
Paper or journal
Pencil

Directions
- Have one student face his or her classmates.
- Tape the ends of the cardboard together to form a headband.
- Insert 5-10 feathers (depending on child's mathematical ability) into the cardboard headband and place it on child's head without the child seeing.
- Tell the student that he or she may ask any one classmate a number question about the feathers that can be answered "yes" or "no." (e.g., "Are there more than _____ feathers? Are there less than _____ feathers? Are there between _____ and _____ feathers?)
- Inform the student wearing the feather headband that he or she may make a guess about the number of feathers in the hat at any time after asking four questions (or fewer if child is able).
- If the guess is correct, allow the student to choose the next headband wearer. If incorrect, give him or her four more question options.

Extensions
1. Assign a child to be "scorekeeper" to tally the number of guesses.
2. This can be played in pairs once the children are confident how the game is played. One child hides his/her eyes while the headband is prepared for wearing. The second child answers questions and tallies the number of questions asked.
3. This can be played alone by merely patterning the colored feathers and recording the pattern in a journal or on a separate piece of paper.

Feather in Your Hat

Use a tally to keep track of the number of questions you need to guess the number of feathers on the headband.

Create a color pattern of two or three different colors of feathers. Copy your pattern in your journal.

Migrating Birds

Skills
Observing
Measuring
Comparing and contrasting
Equalities and inequalities
Communicating

Materials
Styrofoam meat trays, remove rims
Scissors
Permanent marker pens
Ball point pens (for drawing shapes)
Adding machine tape (or string)
Unifix cubes

Directions
- From one tray demonstrate drawing a **circle** for the head and connecting it to a large **oval** for the body. Add **triangle** beak and **circle** eye.
- From second tray, draw and cut wing piece (starting with large **oval**) and **tail** (starting with smaller **oval**).
- Color pieces with permanent pens.
- Slit the bird's body with scissors in two places as illustrated. Insert pieces for wing (A) and tail (B). Adjust wings and tail.
- Have two students fly their bird creations and compare distances by cutting adding machine tape or string the length of the flight. Use Unifix cubes to measure and record in journal.

Literature Link
Gans, Roma. *How Do Birds Find Their Way?* HarperCollins. New York. 1996.

Feathers—Math, Science • Activity 13—Teacher Card

Migrating Birds

- Use a pen to draw a **large** head **circle**, a body **oval**, and a **triangle** beak. Add the neck.
- Draw a large wing **oval** and a small tail **oval**.
- Use colored pens to add eyes and feathers.
- Cut out the bird and the wings and tail.
- Cut a slit for the wing and a slit for the tail.
- Push the wing through the slit inside the body and the tail into the other. Make slits larger if you need to, but not too big!

Feathers • Activity 13—Student Card

© 2004 AIMS Education Foundation

Fly with a Friend

Stand next to each other. Throw your birds one at a time. Stand in your place and have your friend cut the tape (or string) from your foot to where your bird stopped. Now you do the same for your friend. Use Unifix cubes snapped together to measure your tape.

Finish these sentences for your journal:

My bird flew _____ cubes away from me.

My friend's bird flew _____ cubes away.

My bird's flight was _____ (longer, shorter) than my friend's.

Use < or > and write a number sentence.

Feathers • Activity 13—Student Card

Feather Relay

Skills
Observing
Comparing and contrasting
Recalling information

Materials
2 sets of assorted feathers

Directions
- Use two similar sets of feathers.
- Place one set on one side of room and the second set on a table across room.
- Have a child take a feather from one side of the room and walk to the other table to find a match.

Extension
Leave feather on first table. Student must *remember* feather.

Feathers—Science, Game • Activity 14—Teacher Resource Card

Feather Sorting

Skills
Observing
Patterns

Materials
Assorted feathers
AIMS Grouping Circles

Directions
- Use a different color for each circle of the Venn diagram. Overlap the two circles.
- Place assorted feathers beside the Venn.
- Have the child place all feathers of the one color in the left side of the Venn and all feathers of the second color in the right side of the Venn.
- Have students decide where the multi-colored feathers would go in the Venn (in the intersection or outside the Venn diagram).

Extension
Use patterned feathers at left and right.

Feathers—Mathematics, Science • Activity 15—Teacher Resource Card

Feather Sort

Skills
Observing
Comparing and contrasting
Sorting and classifying

Materials
Poster board, one-half piece (22" x14")
Assorted feathers

Directions
- Divide the poster board into thirds.
- Label each section with one of the following categories: flight, down, and body.
- Have children sort feathers into the appropriate categories.

Feathers—Mathematics, Science, Game • Activity 16—Teacher Resource Card

Feather Matching

Skills
Observing
Comparing and contrasting

Materials
Bird pictures
Corresponding feathers

Directions
Match bird pictures and real feathers.

Note
Pictures that correlate with the book *Feather for Lunch* can be used here. However, it is best to use pictures and feathers that are common to your area.

Feathers—Science, Game • Activity 17—Teacher Resource Card

Silhouette Matching

Skills
Observing
Seeing relationships

Materials
Bird pictures
Poster board or file folders
Glue
Hole punch
Shoelace

Background Information
A bird's silhouette may be all you see. It's a quick
way to identify the type of bird.

Directions
These cards can be used for matching or as lacing
cards. For lacing cards, glue enlarged picture on file
folder or poster board. Color and laminate. Cut out
with one-half inch border. Hole punch around the
picture and attach shoelace.

Feathers—Science, Game • Activity 18—Teacher Resource Card

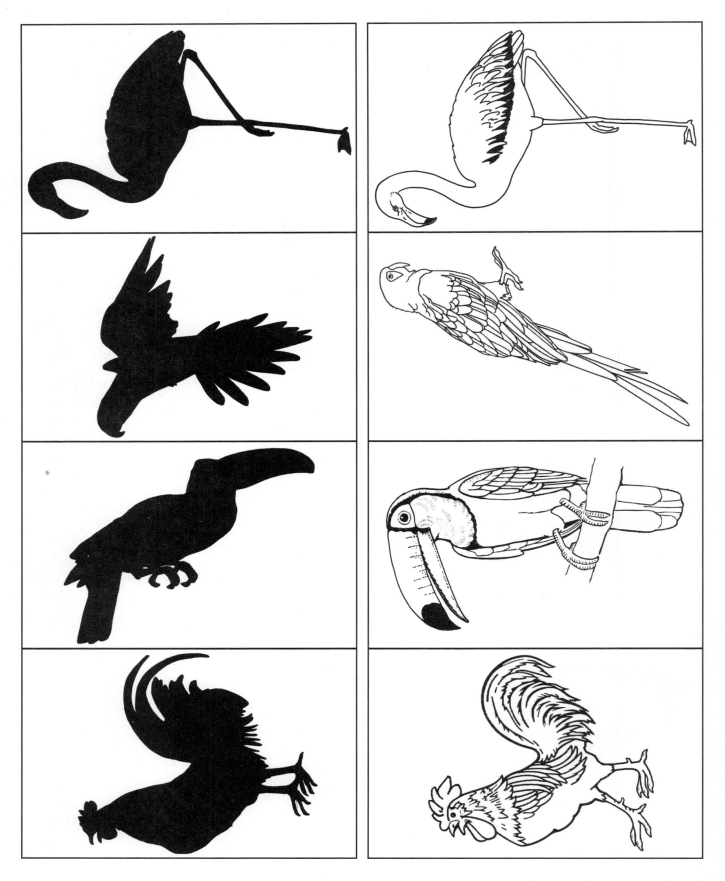

Feathers—Science, Game • Activity 18

Feathers—Science, Game • Activity 18

Feather Fantasies

Skills
Expression of ideas

Materials
Paper

Directions
Children will make framebooks in which sentence starters are given and they create the endings. Have children generate ideas in the different categories. Encourage a specific bird name for the last line. Have children illustrate each page and assemble as a book.

One idea per page
Things I think about feathers:
A feather feels like _____.
A feather can _____.
A feather sounds like _____.
When I drop a feather, it _____.
But a feather doesn't _____.
A feather can't _____.
And I wouldn't use it to _____.
But it works just fine for a _____.

Read *My Feather* by Fiona Pragoff.

Feathers—Literary Link • Activity 19—Teacher Resource Cards

Feather Painting

Skill
Expression of ideas

Materials
Paint
Easel paper
Assorted feathers (flight feathers work best)

Directions
Have students use feathers as paint brushes.

Feathers—Art • Activity 20—Teacher Resource Card

Hide-a-Bird

Skill
Demonstrating understanding of protective coloration

Materials
Wallpaper sample books
Glue
Poster board
Crayons
Scissors
9" x12" manilla paper
Craft sticks

Directions
- Use wallpaper sample books.
- Create habitat scene by gluing wallpaper to a 9" x 12" piece of tag or poster board.
- Encourage children to create a mother bird on a piece of manilla paper with matching coloration so that she'll "blend-in" with background scene.
- Have students cut out and glue the bird onto a craft stick so that the bird can "fly" in and out of the habitat.

Feathers—Science, Art • Activity 21—Teacher Resource Card _ _ _ _ _ _ _ _ _ _ _ _ _ _ _ _ _

Write a Letter to a Bird

Skills
Communicating

Materials
Feathers
Ink, assorted colors
Paper

Directions
- Provide students with hollow flight feathers and different colored inks for children to copy words from the Word Banks.
- Diagonally cut end of quill to form a point.
- Show children how to dip the quill pen into the ink and write.

Extension
Have older children use a letter format to ask questions about habitat, lifestyle, etc.

Feathers—Literary Link, Language • Activity 22— Teacher Resource Card

Light as a Feather Cookies

Skills
Measuring
Sequencing
Observing that matter changes
Using tools

Materials
2 egg whites
$\frac{1}{2}$ teaspoon cream of tartar
$\frac{2}{3}$ cup sugar
Pinch salt
$\frac{1}{2}$ cup chopped pecans
1 cup chocolate chips
1 teaspoon vanilla

Directions
- Preheat oven to 350°.
- Prepare with child's help stirring or use rotary beater so children can take turns.
- Beat egg whites till thick and foamy.
- Add cream of tartar.
- Gradually add sugar and beat till stiff.
- Stir in salt, pecans, and chocolate chips.
- Add vanilla.
- Have children drop small spoonfuls of batter onto a cookie sheet covered with waxed paper.
- Place in oven and turn off oven.
- Leave in oven overnight.
- Makes about 30 cookies.

Feathers—Science, Mathematics, Cooking • Activity 23—Teacher Resource Card

Fly Me

Skills
Observing
Simulating
Comparing and contrasting

Materials
Cardboard boxes
Twill tape or ribbon

Preparation
To make bird wings:
- Cut cardboard boxes into long rectangles (approximately 2 feet in length and 6" – 8" in width).
- Round the top side of each length and jagged cut the bottom side.
- Run 12" pieces of twill tape or ribbon through slits in cardboard at approximately one-third and two-thirds way down the length. These will attach the "wings" to the children's arms.

Extension
Let children paint these to resemble wings.

Note
If you vary the widths, you can identify different bird wing types!
- long and wide—soaring vultures and hawks
- long and narrow—gliding albatross
- wide and rounded—short and fast pheasants
- narrow and pointed—fast swallows

Ask children to compare how the different type wings felt as they "flew."

Feathers—Science • Activity 24—Teacher Resource Card

IT MUST BE A BIRD   54   © 2004 AIMS Education Foundation

Beaks

Background Information

A beak is a bird's tool that is used for catching and eating. A beak's size, thickness, and shape give you clues about the bird's diet and its environment. Although a beak is made up of bone, it is full of blood vessels and sensors, much like our lips.

Often a beak is specialized for a specific kind of food. Seed **crackers** (birds such as sparrows and finches) have short, strong beaks. **Straining** beaks (birds such as flamingos and some ducks) have fine comb-like edges that filter tiny plants and animals from the water. Herons and egrets have beaks to **spear** their prey of fish. Large insect eaters, like the woodpecker, have a **chisel** beak for making holes in trees. Spoonbills and pelicans have a **spoon**-shaped beak for scooping up fish and vegetation in the water. Hummingbirds' hollow beaks protect their special tubular tongue used to extract **(slurp)** nectar from flowers. Toucans have long, thick beaks that are ideal for plucking fruit from trees, while meat eaters' hooked beaks (like those on falcons and eagles) are ideal for **tearing** apart prey that is too big to be eaten whole.

Some birds have unusual beaks. A crow can eat almost anything from lizards to fruit. Its bill is long and sharp yet heavy and thick. The flamingo has a very unusual beak. While most birds have a smaller lower beak that moves against a larger upper beak, the flamingo—a filter feeder—has an upper jaw that moves while the lower jaw stays still. Its fat tongue helps pump water through the sieves of its beak.

Not being able to swallow like humans, birds must throw their heads back to swallow. They, also, do not have teeth to grind up their food. The **crop** in the bird's throat is like a bag where food goes to be stored and softened. Food then passes to the gizzard. The **gizzard** acts like our teeth as a grinding machine. It uses stones that the bird has swallowed to help break up what it has eaten. In owls, which swallow their prey whole, the gizzard wraps up the parts that are indigestible (like fur, bone, and teeth) and later the owl coughs up a **pellet** with these items neatly wrapped in feathers.

Although some gardeners and farmers try to scare off birds that eat their crops, birds that eat insects and rodents are especially welcomed.

Types of Beaks

Cracking

Slurping

Tearing

Chiseling

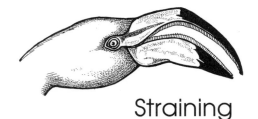

Straining

Beak Vocabulary

cracking beak	straining beak
chiseling beak	spooning beak
tearing beak	slurping beak
crop	spearing beak
owl pellet	gizzard

Use this vocabulary in context. Provide word banks in the language area for creative writing. Add illustrations for the non-reader or emerging reader. Add definitions for the beginning reader.

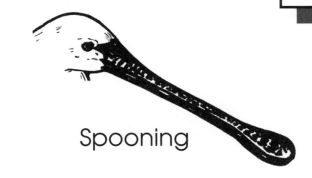

Spooning

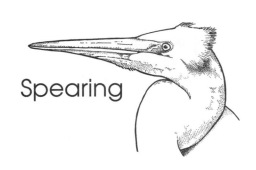

Spearing

Introductory Activity
—Beaks

Topic
Birds' beaks

Key Question
Why do different birds have different kinds of beaks?

Focus
Students will use various tools and compare their usefulness in picking up different kinds of foods.

Guiding Documents
Project 2061 Benchmarks
- *Plants and animals both need to take in water, and animals need to take in food.*
- *Different plants and animals have external features that help them thrive in different kinds of places.*
- *Simple graphs can help to tell about observations.*
- *Shapes such as circles, squares and triangles can be used to describe many things that can be seen.*
- *Things in nature and things people make have very different sizes, weights, ages, and speeds.*

NRC Standards
The Characteristics of Organisms
- *Organisms have basic needs. For example, animals need air, water, and food; plants require air, water, nutrients, and light. Organisms can survive only in environments in which their needs can be met. The world has many different environments, and distinct environments support the life of different types of organisms.*
- *Each plant or animal has different structures that serve different functions in growth, survival, and reproduction.*
- *The behavior of individual organisms is influenced by internal cues (such as hunger) and by external cues (such as a change in the environment). Humans and other organisms have senses that help them detect internal and external cues.*

NCTM Standards 2000*
- *Count with understanding and recognize "how many" in sets of objects*
- *Represent data using concrete objects, pictures, and graphs*

Science
Life science
    characteristics of organisms
    organisms and environments

Math
Charting
Counting
Equalities and inequalities

Integrated Processes
Observing
Comparing and contrasting
Inferring
Communicating

Materials
Large writing surface (poster board or butcher wrap)
Permanent pens of different colors
Masking tape
Sticky notes
Clothespin
Scissors
Toothpick
Spoon
Raisins
Macaroni pieces
Styrofoam peanuts
Marbles
Dish of water

Management

1. This is an introductory (modeling) exercise. Be sure to allow all students to explore the different tools and how they affect the type of "food" eaten by the birds with different bills.
2. Task Cards in this section will allow for further exploration of beak types.

Procedure

Part One (Total Group Activity—Teacher directed)

1. Tell the children, "Today we are going to be a special kind of scientist. We are going to **observe** (look at) different kinds of beaks. We will **compare** these beaks and then make good guesses (**inferences**) about what kinds of food these birds might eat with their special beaks."
2. Use Large Eyewitness Book, *Birds* by David Burnie, or a series of large photos of birds with different types of beaks. Show the pictures.
3. Illicit from the children descriptive words about the beak(s). Write each term on chart paper using a different colored pen and draw a line from the central term **Beak** and add a quick sketch. Encourage children to note relative length, thickness, and shape. Compare top and bottom beak. (Are they the same size? ...shape?)

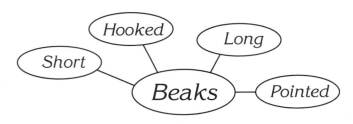

4. If they know what that bird eats, add that picture with a sticky note (e.g., worm) next to that beak.
5. At close of session, have children draw a bird eating something with its special beak. Date their pictures for their portfolios.

Part Two

1. Have each child share his or her picture from *Part One*.
2. Introduce the following activity. Have a tray ready with four plastic cups and four "bird tools": clothespin, scissors, toothpick, and spoon.
3. Choose four children and ask them to each pick **one** bird tool. Have the rest of class form a circle around the four children and tray.
4. Demonstrate the following
   - opening and closing the clothespin as wide as possible. (*"Which bird might this be?"*)
   - holding the scissors with the points down and opening and closing like tweezers (not stabbing). (*"Which bird might this be?"*)
   - "spearing" with the toothpick with one hand and removing the food by pushing off with the other hand. (*"Which bird might this be?"*)
   - holding the end of the spoon with one hand and scooping up. (*"Which bird might this be?"*)
5. Give each child one plastic cup. Inform the students that the cups will be the bird's "crop" where food is stored until it can be safely eaten later.
6. When the four children are comfortable with their "bird tool," scatter macaroni pieces in the center of the tray. Direct each child in turn to use their tool to try to pick up food for their "crop" cup. Continue until all food is gone. Ask children which tools worked best for the macaroni "worms."
7. Repeat the process with marble "snails."
8. Repeat with raisin "grubs."
9. Pour some water into the tray so that the Styrofoam peanuts float. Now repeat the feeding process with the floating Styrofoam as "water bugs."
10. Have each child empty the "crop" cup onto his or her "tool" graph. Discuss.
    a. Which beak worked best for which food?
    b. Which beak worked best for more than one food?
11. Show a picture of a hummingbird (specialist beak). Inform the student that its special beak is used for getting nectar from flowers. Ask the students where they think this bird would need to live?
12. Show a picture of a blue jay (generalist beak). Tell the students that this bird eats seeds, insects, frogs, eggs. Ask where this bird could live?

---

* Reprinted with permission from *Principles and Standards for School Mathematics,* 2000 by the National Council of Teachers of Mathematics. All rights reserved.

Graphs

_____
Child's name

Toothpick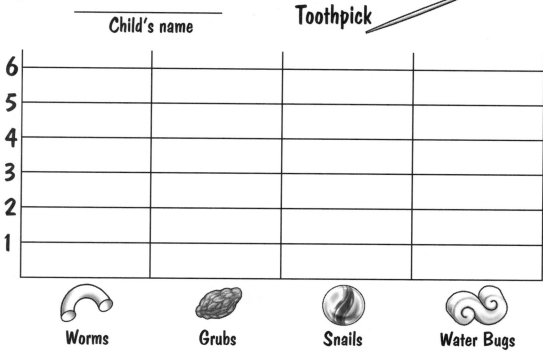

6			
5			
4			
3			
2			
1			

Worms   Grubs   Snails   Water Bugs

_____
Child's name

Clothespin

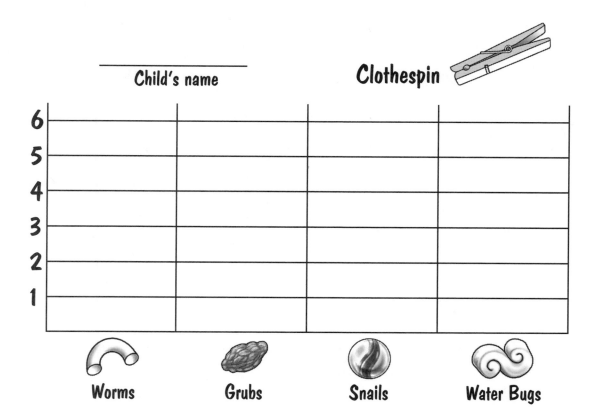

6			
5			
4			
3			
2			
1			

Worms   Grubs   Snails   Water Bugs

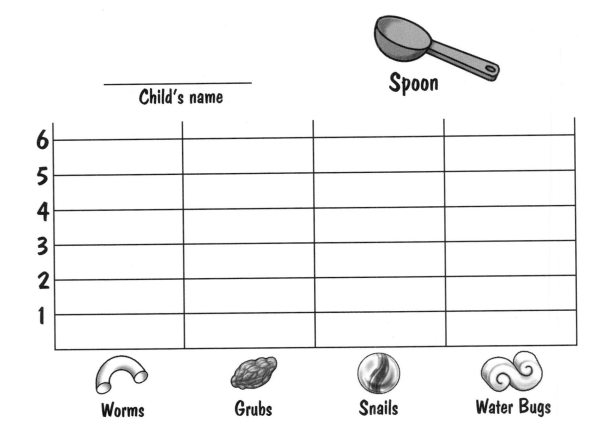

Child's name _____

Spoon

6
5
4
3
2
1

Worms   Grubs   Snails   Water Bugs

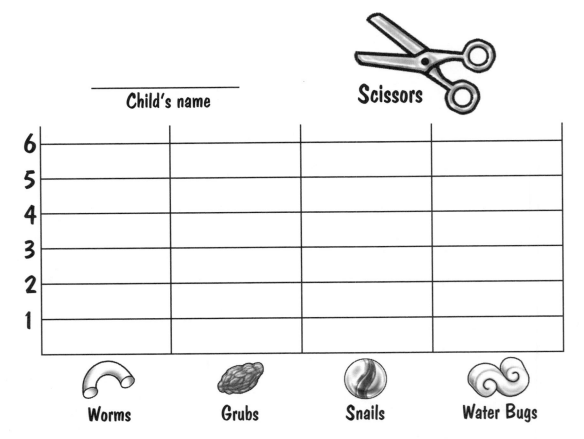

Child's name _____

Scissors

6
5
4
3
2
1

Worms   Grubs   Snails   Water Bugs

Beaks
(Tune: "Ants Go Marching")
—by Donna VanderWeide

(Have corresponding pictures for each bird. Allow children to make up motions to go with each beak.)

My beak is short and strong, I go chomp, chomp—chomp, chomp.
My beak is short and strong, I go chomp, chomp—chomp, chomp.
My beak is short and strong, indeed.
It's perfect to break open seeds
And I like to fly around, to look, for seeds all day.

(Grosbeak, sparrow, finch, cardinal)

Grosbeak

My beak is long and flat, I go splash, splash—splash, splash.
My beak is long and flat, I go splash, splash—splash, splash.
My beak is long and flat. I need
To scoop up fish from out of the sea,
And I separate the fish, from weeds, to get the food I need.

(Spoonbills and pelicans)

Spoonbill

Heron

My beak is long and very sharp—stab, stab—stab, stab.
My beak is long and very sharp—stab, stab—stab, stab.
My beak is long and sharp, it's true.
I'm after fish and frogs for food,
And I wade in water, slow, to fool, the fish I eat.

(Heron)

Eagle

My beak is strong and has a hook—rip, rip—rip, rip.
My beak is strong and has a hook—rip, rip—rip, rip.
My beak is strong. Its hook for me
Helps tear up meat that I can eat,
And I soar along in the sky, with my talons ready to grab.

(Eagles and hawks)

My beak is hollow; it hides my tongue—slurp, slurp—slurp, slurp.
My beak is hollow; it hides my tongue—slurp, slurp—slurp, slurp.
My beak is hollow; it hides my tongue.
I drink sweet nectar until I am done,
And I roll up my tongue, and I slurp it right on through.

(Hummingbird)

Hummingbird

Now you have teeth with different jobs, it's true—it's true.
Now you have teeth with different jobs, it's true—it's true.
You can cut and tear and mash and grind.
You'd make a great crow if you had a mind
Just remember not to try, to fly, without your wings.

*(Crow and **child**)*

Beak Task Cards

Topic
Properties of beaks

Key Question
How do we sort and group beaks?

Focus
The students will note similarities and differences in beaks and group them accordingly.

Guiding Documents
Project 2061 Benchmarks
- *People can often learn about things around them by just observing those things carefully, but sometimes they can learn more by doing something to the things and noting what happens.*
- *Tools such as thermometers, magnifiers, rulers or balances often give more information about things than can be obtained by just observing things without their help.*
- *Describing things as accurately as possible is important in science because it enables people to compare their observations with those of others.*
- *When people give different descriptions of the same thing, it is usually a good idea to make some fresh observations instead of just arguing about who is right.*
- *Tools are used to do things better or more easily and to do some things that could not otherwise be done at all. In technology, tools are used to observe, measure, and make things.*
- *When trying to build something or to get something to work better, it usually helps to follow directions if there are any or to ask someone who has done it before for suggestions.*
- *People are more likely to believe your ideas if you can give good reasons for them.*
- *Describe and compare things in terms of number, shape, texture, size, weight, color, and motion.*
- *Draw pictures that correctly portray at least some features of the thing being described.*

NRC Standards
- *Scientists use different kinds of investigations depending on the questions they are trying to answer. Types of investigations include describing objects, events, and organisms; classifying them; and doing a fair test (experimenting).*
- *Simple instruments, such as magnifiers, thermometers, and rulers, provide more information than scientists obtain using only their senses.*
- *Organisms have basic needs. For example, animals need air, water, and food; plants require air, water, nutrients, and light. Organisms can survive only in environments in which their needs can be met.*
- *Each plant or animal has different structures that serve different functions in growth, survival, and reproduction.*

NCTM Standards 2000*
- *Count with understanding and recognize "how many" in sets of objects*
- *Represent data using concrete objects, pictures, and graphs*
- *Use tools to measure*

Science
Life science
    characteristics of organisms
    organisms and environments

Math
Measuring
Counting
Graphing

Integrated Processes
Observing
Communicating
Comparing and contrasting
Classifying

Materials (see *Task Cards*)
Toilet tissue rolls
Colored construction paper
Camera and film
Sunflower seeds and kernels
Resealable plastic bags
Aquarium gravel
Small aquarium net
Sand

Small pebbles
Egg timer (sand)
Tall thin vase
Scissors
Spoons
Slotted spoon
Bowls
Puffed rice
Oatmeal
Raisins
Assorted whole nuts
Dry rice
Curly noodles
Grapes on the stem
Loose tea leaves
Nutcracker
Chopsticks
Tweezers
Tongs
Decorative bark or small log
Glue
String
Permanent pen
Water dish
Tea strainer
Styrofoam pieces
Crackers

Management

1. You may
   - Run these task cards on colored tagboard to code them for different tasks (e.g. all *beak* experiences one color or all *math* same color). Laminate and fold in half so that student side is showing in centers, or
   - Duplicate and mount on file folder or large index card. (Student directions on one side and teacher directions on the other.) Color and laminate.
2. The cards are intended for learning stations.
3. Introduce one task card.
4. Demonstrate the directions printed on the card for the children.
5. If there is a drawing or written response expected, model that also. If a model is made, leave yours at the station so children may refer to it.
6. If interest remains high at a station, leave it for the children when you add the next station. Stations may be set up on a special table or on a cookie sheet or serving tray placed in an out-of-the-way place in your classroom, preferably near a window.
7. Note: In the set of station cards, there are *Teacher Cards* that do not have an accompanying *Student Card*. These stations consist of centers or games that you can set up for the children and only require verbal directions and modeling from the teacher.

* Reprinted with permission from *Principles and Standards for School Mathematics,* 2000 by the National Council of Teachers of Mathematics. All rights reserved.

A-Beak-A-Minute

Skills
Observing
Comparing and contrasting
Using tools
Measuring
One-to-one correspondence
Graphing

Materials
Egg (sand) timer
"Crop" cup
Paper or journal
Pencil
Beak tools—clothespin, scissors, toothpick, spoon
Assorted "foods"—macaroni (worms), raisins
   (grubs), marbles (snails), Styrofoam pieces
   floating in water (water bugs)

Directions
* Have first child choose a "tool" and a "food" and
  place them on a tray.
* Direct second child to start the egg timer and
  say, "GO!" at which time the first child picks
  up and places as many pieces of food with the
  chosen tool as he/she can in the "crop" cup
  before second child says, "Stop" when the sand
  runs out.
* Have both students count the number of food
  pieces captured in the time allowed. Direct them to
  record their count in their journal and on a graph.
* Have students switch roles for the same food and tool.
* Allow students to repeat the process with
  different foods.
* Then have students choose another tool and repeat.

(Provide a graph for each child.)

I used _____ as a tool.

Food

Beaks—Mathematics, Science, Paired Activity • Activity 1—Teacher Card

A-Beak-A-Minute

1. **Child One:**
   Pick one tool and one food.

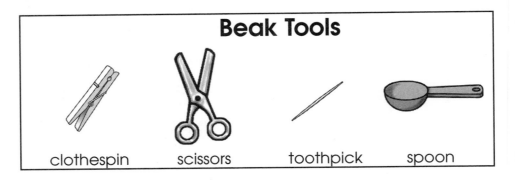

Beak Tools

clothespin   scissors   toothpick   spoon

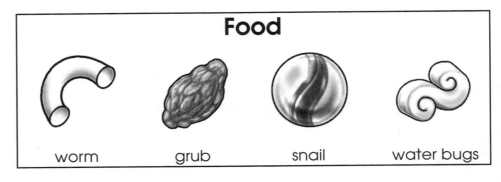

Food

worm   grub   snail   water bugs

2. **Child Two:**
   Set the timer and say "Go" to start and "Stop" when timer is empty.

3. **Child One and Child Two:**
   Count together what is caught and put in the crop cup. Record your results.

4. **Child One and Child Two:**
   Switch roles and do it again.

5. **Child One and Child Two:**
   Compare your results.

A-Beak-A-Minute

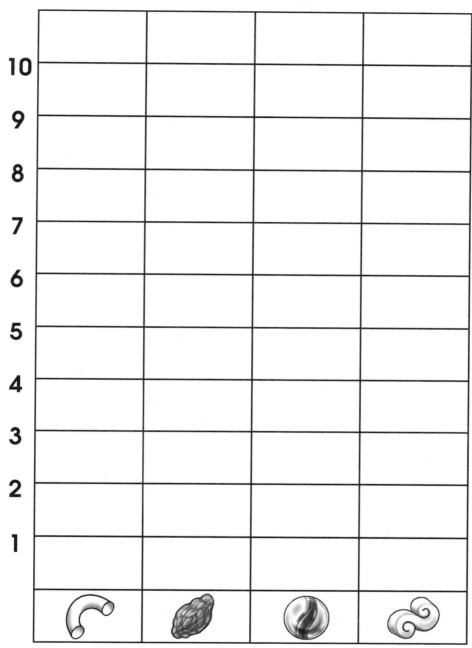

10
9
8
7
6
5
4
3
2
1

Food

Choose a tool

Beaks • Activity 1—Student Card

Picture Beaks

Skills
Observing
Using tools
Communicating

Materials
Assorted tubes from toilet paper rolls, paper towels, etc.
Assorted construction paper
Glue
Scissors
Paint
Brushes
Markers
Camera
Paper or journal
Pencil
Hole punch
String

Directions
- Provide pictures of various bird beaks for children to see easily. Be sure pictures are labeled with the names of the birds.
- Cut tubes into assorted lengths.
- Have children create different bills by gluing construction paper onto tubes or by coloring tubes with paint or markers into size and shape of bills.
- When tubes are finished, punch a hole in the tube and tie string so that the child can wear the beak.
- Take a picture of each child with the beak on.
- Scribe what the child says about what the "bird" eats and what its name is.
- Display pictures and descriptions in classroom and/or make a class book.

Extension
Children may write their own book, "A Meal with a Bird," about a day of hunting for food (as a bird), or they can ask the teacher to scribe their narrative. This can be a journal or blank book experience.

Beaks—Science, Literary Link, Paired Activity • Activity 2—Teacher Card

Picture Beaks

Choose a beak to make over a tube. You may use paper, paint, or markers.

Have your teacher take a picture of you. Tell her/him your story or write your own.

Beaks—Science, Literary Link, Paired Activity • Activity 2—Student Card

Gizzard Grinders

Skills
Observing
Comparing and contrasting
Predicting
Drawing conclusions

Materials
Sunflower seeds
Sunflower kernels
Nutcracker
2 resealable plastic bags
Water
Aquarium gravel
Sand
Small pebbles
Kitchen timer
Permanent pen
1 tablespoon
1 teaspoon

Directions
- Use a permanent marking pen to label one of the plastic bags *Gizzard*. Label the other bag *Crop*.
- Place the aquarium gravel in the bag marked *Gizzard*.
- Place one tablespoon of sunflower kernels in the plastic bag marked *Crop*. Add one teaspoon of water and seal the bag.
- Set the timer for 30 minutes.
- When timer goes off, open bag and add one teaspoon of aquarium gravel from bag marked *Gizzard*. Close the crop bag.
- Have students rub first bag together and compare kernels appearance before and after rubbing.

Extension
Vary
a) size of grinding material (sand to small stones),
b) soaking time, or
c) try with unshelled seeds.

Beaks—Science • Activity 3—Teacher Card

Gizzard Grinders

Step 1

Put large spoon of kernels in the "crop" bag.

Step 2

Add a small spoon of water to your "crop" bag.

Step 3

Close the bag.

Step 4

Set timer to 30 minutes.

Step 5

When timer goes off, open the "crop" bag and add a small spoon of gravel from the "gizzard" bag.

Step 6
Close the "crop" bag.

Step 7

Rub the contents of the "crop" bag with your hands.

Step 8

What happened? Make your picture to show what you have done.

Beaks • Activity 3—Student Card

Gizzard Grinders

by: _____

Step 1
Draw what you see.

Step 2
Add water.

Step 5
This is the crop and water and gizzard rocks.

This is the crop and water and gizzard rocks and me.

Step 6
Then I did this:

Step 7
Then I did this:

What happened?

What else can I do?

Flamingo Food

Skills
Observing
Drawing conclusions
Predicting

Materials
Loose tea leaves
2 spoons
Dish of water
Tea strainer
Tray
Crackers
Pictures of flamingos

Information
Flamingos feed with their heads upside down. Their upper jaw moves and their lower jaw stays still. Their beaks have rows of horny plates that strain the edibles from the water. Their thick tongues pump very rapidly to push out the water.

Directions
- Demonstrate for the children how to stir one spoon of tea leaves into water and then use tea strainer to lift out as many leaves as possible. The second spoon is used to press the water out of the tea leaves to model how the flamingo uses its tongue to push out the water.
- Child may need to stir water again to retrieve all of the leaves. (The flamingo often stamps its feet while standing in the water to stir up the food found on the bottom of the lake.)

Extension
Let children act out being a flamingo with an "upside down" jaw. Compare how their jaw moves when they chew a cracker "right-side up" and then when they hang their head "upside-down" and chew.

Beaks—Science • Activity 4—Teacher Card

Flamingo Food

1. Stir one spoon of leaves into the bowl of water.

2. Use the strainer to remove as many leaves as you can.

3. Use the second spoon to squeeze the water out of the leaves.

4. Clean out the strainer.

5. Stir the water and try again.

Try This
Sit on a chair. Ask a friend to watch you chew a cracker while you are sitting upright. Then ask your friend to watch you chew the cracker with your head upside-down, like a flamingo. Tell your friend how you felt. Ask your friend how you looked.

Food Court for Birds

Skills
Observing
Using science tools
Comparing and contrasting
Communicating

Materials
For each of the seven stations:
   a tray and a tool: straw, chopsticks, nutcracker,
      slotted spoon, strainer, tweezers, tongs
   a task card (laminated or in a plastic bag)
   "bird foods" and "habitat settings"

Foods and Habitats
1. Water colored with red food coloring in a tall, thin vase
2. Bowl with dry oatmeal and raisins
3. Whole nuts on leaves and sticks
4. Bowl of water and styrofoam pieces
5. Bowl of water and small dish of puffed rice
6. Dry rice and curly noodles on bark
7. Grapes on a stem in a bowl

Directions
Food Court for Birds consists of seven stations that model how different birds eat. Mount the *Teacher Card* on the outside of a file folder and the *Student Card* on the inside.

For younger children, demonstrate the use of the beak "tool" at each station. Discuss with children what each tool represents in the real world. For older children, they can experiment with different tools. These stations can be done on several days with one or two stations per day or as a special one-day emphasis.

Procedure
Use a large table and set up stations around the table or set up stations along a long wall. Each child moves in one direction from one station to the next trying each tool from each tray.

(The stations are an adaptation of "Fit the Bill" from *Birds, Birds, Birds. Ranger Rick's Nature Scope.* National Wildlife Federation, Washington, DC. 1985.)

Hummingbird Smoothie

Skills
Observing

Materials
Red-colored water
Tall thin vase
Straw
Tray

Directions
- Set up a tray with colored water in a tall, thin vase to represent nectar in a flower. The straw is used as the beak tool.
- Demonstrate dipping the straw into water and placing one finger over the end of straw. Lift up the straw until it is even with the top of the vase and remove your finger. ("Nectar" will flow back into vase.)
- Caution children *not* to sip the liquid up this straw as the straw will be used over and over by classmates! (Have spares for those who "forget"!)

Beaks—Science Content • Activity 5 — Teacher Card (Station 1 of 7 "Food Court for Birds")

Hummingbird Smoothie

Bird Fact:

Hummingbirds drink nectar from flowers.

Use the straw and your finger to lift nectar from the flower (vase).

Soupy Snipe

Skills
Observing

Materials
Bowl of dry oatmeal
Raisins
Chopsticks
Tray

Directions
- Set up the tray with a bowl of dry oatmeal and raisins at the bottom of bowl ("worms in the mud"). The chopsticks are used as the beak tool.
- Demonstrate using the chopsticks to probe for raisins "worms" on the bottom. Pull out at least three raisins.
- Encourage children to replace raisins in bottom of bowl before they leave the station.

Soupy Snipe

 Bird Fact:

Snipes use their long beaks to dip for worms and small creatures in the mud and water.

Use the chopstick to dig for raisin "worms." Try to find at least three. When you are through, replace your raisins at the bottom of the oatmeal "mud."

Grosbeak Cracklins

Skills
Observing

Materials
Assorted whole nuts
Dish of leaves and sticks
Nutcracker
Tray

Directions
- Set up the tray with assorted whole nuts on the dish of leaves and sticks. The nutcracker is used as the beak tool.
- Demonstrate cracking open one nut with the nutcracker. (Children may eat the nutmeat, if they want to. Be aware of any food allergies to nuts. If such a case exists, do not let any students eat the nutmeats.)
- Encourage them to discard any shells or leftover nutmeats so the habitat is ready for the next "bird."

Beaks—Science Content • Activity 7—Teacher Card (Station 3 of 7 "Food Court for Birds")

Grosbeak Cracklins

Bird Fact:

Grosbeaks have short, strong beaks to crack open seeds.

Choose one nut to crack open with the nutcracker. Please throw shell pieces and leftover nuts in the trash before going to the next station.

Beaks • Food Court 3 • Activity 7

Pelican Poppers

Skills
Observing

Materials
Bowl of water
Styrofoam pieces
Slotted spoon
Tray

Directions
- Set up the tray with a bowl of water with Styrofoam pieces floating in it. The slotted spoon is used as the beak tool.
- Demonstrate lifting the pieces from the water with the slotted spoon.
- Ask, "What happens to the water? … to the pieces?"
- Have students replace pieces in water.

Beaks—Science Content • Activity 8—Teacher Card (Station 4 of 7 "Food Court for Birds")

Pelican Poppers

Bird Fact: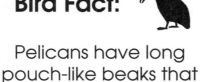

Pelicans have long pouch-like beaks that can scoop up fish from the water.

Use the slotted spoon to lift up the styrofoam pieces from the water. See what happens to the water. See what happens to the pieces. Replace the pieces in the water before moving to the next station.

Beaks • Food Court 4 • Activity 8

Flamingo Fish

Skills
Observing

Materials
Large bowl of water
Small bowl puffed rice
Small aquarium net
Tray

Directions
- Set up the tray with the large bowl of water and a small bowl of puffed rice. The small aquarium net is used as the beak tool.
- Demonstrate tossing a small amount of puffed rice into the water. Use the net to retrieve the rice.
- Have students discard wet rice when through.

Flamingo Fish

Bird Fact:
Flamingos have bills that act as strainers that leave small water animals and plants for flamingos to eat.

Toss a pinch of puffed rice into the water. Use the net to "fish" it out. Throw the wet rice away before moving to the next station.

Beaks • Food Court 5 • Activity 9

Warbler Rice

Skills
Observing

Materials
Piece of bark or small log
Dry rice and dry curly noodles
Tweezers
Tray

Directions
- Set up tray with a piece of decorative bark or a small log. Spread dry rice and curly noodles on top. The tweezers are used as the beak tool.
- Demonstrate picking up rice and noodles using tweezers only.

Warbler Rice

Bird Fact:
Warblers have small, sharp-pointed beaks for picking up insects from leaves, logs, and twigs.

Use the tweezers *only* and pick up rice and noodle "worms" from log.

Toucan Tummy Toucher

Skills
Observing

Materials
Bowl of grapes on stem
Tongs
Tray

Directions
- Set up tray with the bowl of grapes on the stem. The tongs are used as the beak tool.
- Demonstrate using *only* the tongs to pull grapes off the stem. Hold the grape bunch with the other hand just as a toucan uses its foot!

Beaks—Science Content • Activity 11—Teacher Card (Station 7 of 7 "Food Court for Birds")

Toucan Tummy Toucher

Bird Fact:

Toucans have long, thick beaks for pulling fruit from trees.

Use the tongs with one hand and pull off five grapes. You may eat them if you'd like!

Beaks • Food Court 7 • Activity 11

Beak Sort

Skills
Observing
Comparing and contrasting
Sorting and classifying

Materials
Chart
Assorted bird pictures

Directions
- Enlarge chart onto poster board or large paper. Laminate.
- Have assorted bird pictures available for children to sort into the different categories.

Extension
What kind of food would each beak eat? Use pictures of insects, rodents, seeds to sort.

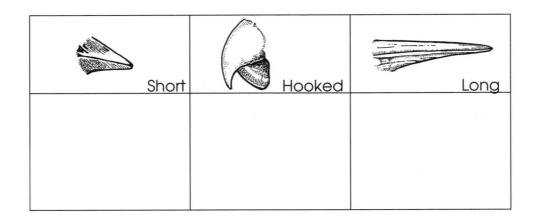

Short	Hooked	Long

Beak Sort

Chart *

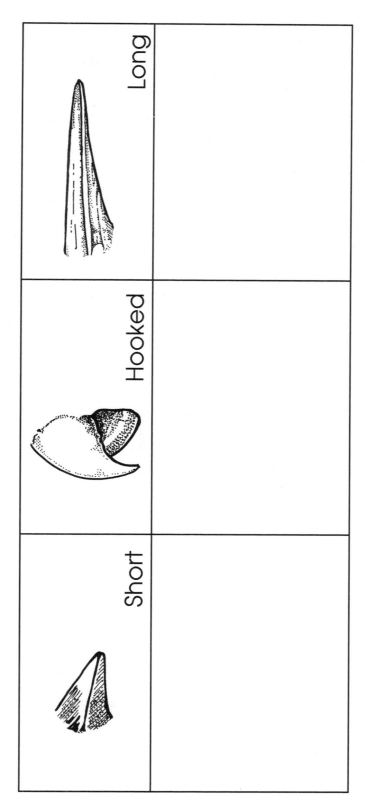

Long	Hooked	Short

* Enlarge on poster board and laminate.

Talking Bird Books

Skill
Communicating

Materials
9" x 12" construction paper
Scissors
Glue
Markers
Tactile materials

Directions
Fold construction paper in half. Cut slit in middle.
Fold and crease one side of the slit down.
Fold and crease the other side of the slit up.
Turn folded paper over and fold and crease the other way.
Push folds to the inside to form a beak.
Add additional details (two eyes, two legs, feathers, etc.).

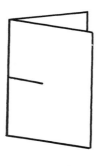

Step 1

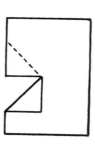

Step 2

Step 3

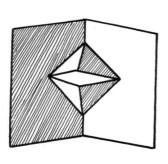

Step 5

Step 6

Can You Guess what I Am Eating

Skills
Observing
Seeing relationships

Materials
6" x 18" paper
Markers

Directions
Fold 6" x 18" paper in half.
Fold the right section back in half again.
On left side draw body of the bird.
Draw its beak on the flap.
Open up the right flap and draw the beak again—
    this time with food in it! Answer the riddle, "What
    do I eat?"

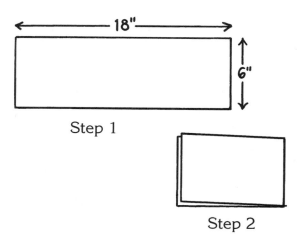

Step 1

Step 2

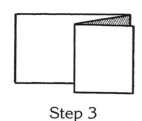

Step 3

Step 4

Step 5

Making Chicken Feed

Skills
Observing
Graphing
Counting
Comparing and contrasting
Equalitites and inequalities

Materials
Choose one recipe to make:

Recipe #1
12-oz mixed nuts
1 cup chopped dried apple
$1\frac{1}{2}$ cup dark raisins
1 cup roasted hulled sunflower kernels

Recipe #2
2 cups round cereal
1 cup peanuts
$\frac{1}{2}$ cup sunflower seeds
$\frac{1}{2}$ cup raisins

For either recipe:
large bowl
small portion cups

Directions
- Make a graph to go with the chosen recipe. Label each column with the name of an ingredient.
- Have children help measure and mix the above ingredients from one of the recipes.
- Using small portion cups, allow children to scoop out one measure and lay parts on their graph.
- Discuss which ingredient of the "chicken feed" they made had the most pieces? … the least? … the same?

Extension
Have children color in graph. Write equations for addition and subtraction in their journals about the comparative values of their graph.

Discuss
How many hard items?…soft items?…seeds?, etc.

Chicken Feed Graph

11					
10					
9					
8					
7					
6					
5					
4					
3					
2					
1					

Round Cereal   Peanuts   Sunflower Seeds   Raisins   Dried Apple

Beaks—Mathematics, Science • Activity 15—"Gorp Graphing" Teacher Resource Card

Feed-A-Bird

Skills
Observing
Measuring
Comparing and contrasting

Materials
1 cup cornmeal
1 cup flour
1 cup bread crumbs
$\frac{1}{2}$ t. soda
$\frac{3}{4}$ cup raisins
$\frac{1}{4}$ t. sand
$\frac{1}{2}$ cup bacon drippings
1 cup water

Directions
- Combine cornmeal, flour, bread crumbs, and soda.
- Add raisins and sand.
- Pour in bacon drippings and water and mix well.
- Spoon into muffin tins.
- Bake at 350° for 15 minutes.
- Serve on a feeder tray or impale on branches.
- Discuss with the children what makes this recipe unfit for humans!

Beaks—Mathematics, Science • Activity 16—"Feed-A-Bird" Teacher Resource Card

Beak Breakfasts Game
Food Card Game

Copy the game components (next page) onto colored paper. Cut out the components and glue as illustrated onto a file folder. Laminate the game. Assemble the Game Cube. The key tells how far to move after you've matched food to beak shown on cube. Unifix cubes can be used by players for markers.

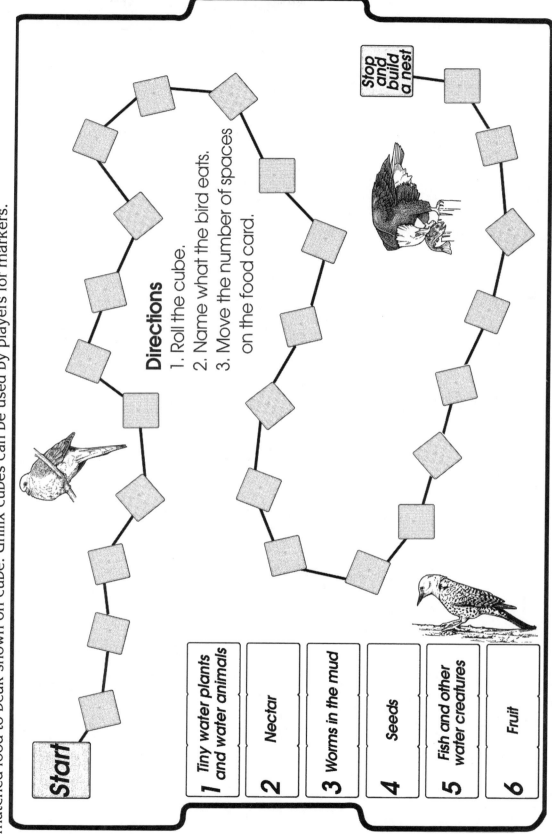

Directions

1. Roll the cube.
2. Name what the bird eats.
3. Move the number of spaces on the food card.

Start

Stop and build a nest

1	Tiny water plants and water animals
2	Nectar
3	Worms in the mud
4	Seeds
5	Fish and other water creatures
6	Fruit

Beak Breakfasts Game

Food Card Components

Directions:
1. Roll the cube.
2. Name what the bird eats.
3. Move the number of spaces on the food card.

Start

Stop and build a nest

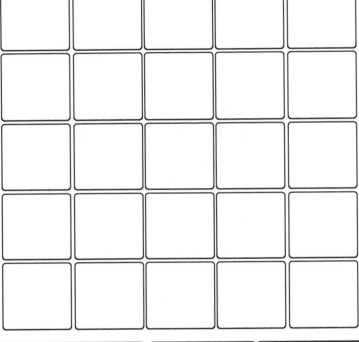

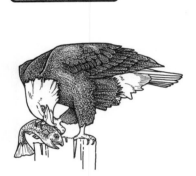

1	*Tiny water plants and water animals*	**4**	*Seeds*
2	*Nectar*	**5**	*Fish and other water creatures*
3	*Worms in the mud*	**6**	*Fruit*

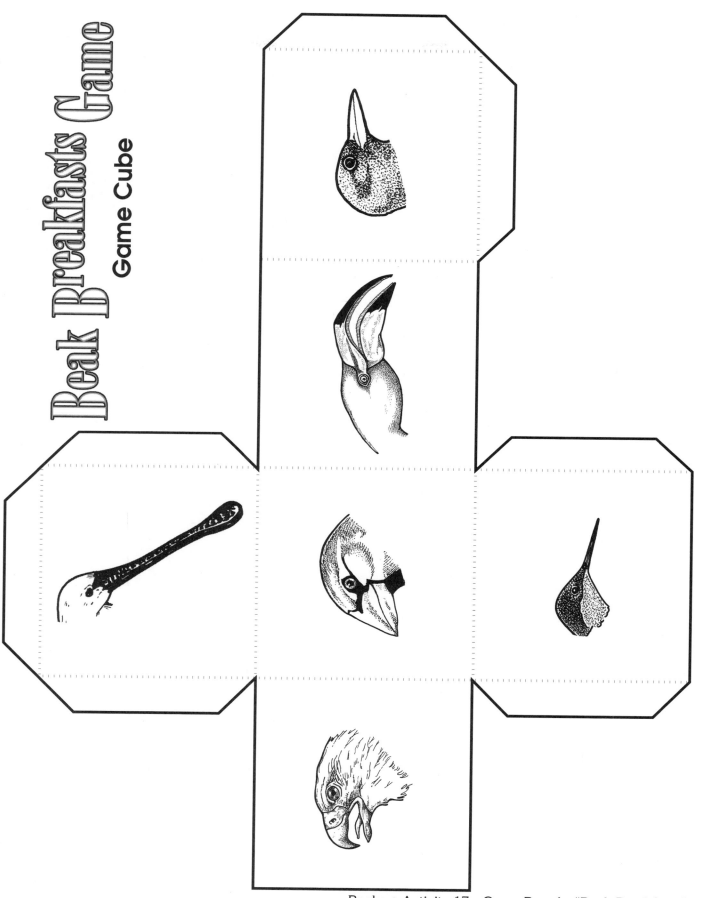

Beaks • Activity 17—Game Board—"Beak Breakfasts"

Background Information

Bird feet give clues about habitats and food-gathering techniques. Most birds have three or four toes with the most common configuration being three toes forward and one toe back.

The single hind toe structure allows birds to grip a branch or other type of perch. **Perching** bird legs have tendons that act like pulleys that tighten and clamp toes onto the branch. Because of this, these birds are able to stay perched while asleep. To release the foot, toe muscles must contract so that the bird can lift off. Half of the world's bird species has feet adapted for **perching** (songbirds, robins, and the chicken).

Some birds like owls, parrots, woodpeckers, and roadrunners have two toes forward and two toes back, creating an x-shaped track pattern. The two back toes help enable the woodpeckers and nuthatches to anchor themselves to the bark of trees while climbing.

Eagles, hawks, vultures, and owls use their sharp, curved **talons** to catch their prey. These birds can spread their toes wide to form a **grasping grip** that enables them to catch, hold, and carry heavy weights below their bodies and away from their wings. Many of these birds have feathers that extend down to their ankles. These feathers help to silence their flight as they approach their prey.

Wading birds, such as herons and egrets, have long toes and legs that keep them from sinking in soft mud while wading in ponds and streams.

Loons, ducks, geese and swans have **webbed** feet that are ideal for paddling and **swimming**. They often use these wide feet as brakes when landing on water.

Birds move along the ground in two ways, hopping and walking. Smaller birds move by hopping; they can easily lift their body weight by flexing their feet. Larger birds transfer their weight from foot to foot when walking. A glimpse of bird tracks in wet mud or snow will provide evidence of the bird's walking style. The two tracks of a hopping bird will be side by side, while the two tracks of a walking bird will be positioned one ahead of the other. Some birds show fancy foot work, such as the goose that walks with a toe-in **waddle** or the rock pigeon's circular courting dance.

Birds that rarely land (like swifts) have very weak legs; whereas, flightless birds (like the ostrich) have very muscular legs. Ostriches can reach speeds of up to 45 miles per hour when running after prey.

Birds legs are mainly bone and tendons surrounded by **scaly** skin. The muscles at the top of the leg keep the strength of the leg near the body. Cold climate birds conserve body heat by not wasting it on long legs.

While a bird's feathers are often thought to be the colorful portion of the bird, there is also great variety in the coloration of birds' feet. Colors of feet vary from the yellow feet of the finch to the bright orange of the starling's.

Grasping

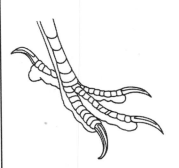
Perching

Wading

Bird Feet Vocabulary

perching	claws
climbing	grasping
wading	webbed
swimming	prey
waddle	scaly

Use this vocabulary in context. Provide word banks in the language area for creative writing. Add illustrations for the non-reader or emerging reader. Add definitions for the beginning reader.

Climbing

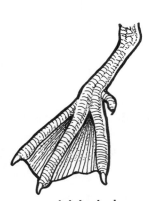
Webbed
Swimming

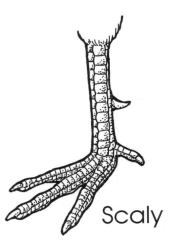
Scaly

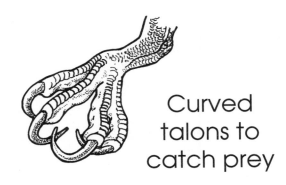
Curved
talons to
catch prey

Introductory Activity—Feet

Topic
Bird Locomotion

Key Question
How do different birds move?

Focus
Students will compare the different ways birds move.

Guiding Documents
Project 2061 Benchmarks
- *People can often learn about things around them by just observing those things carefully, but sometimes they can learn more by doing something to the things and noting what happens.*
- *Tools such as thermometers, magnifiers, rulers or balances often give more information about things than can be obtained by just observing things without their help.*
- *Describing things as accurately as possible is important in science because it enables people to compare their observations with those of others.*
- *When people give different descriptions of the same thing, it is usually a good idea to make some fresh observations instead of just arguing about who is right.*

All students, especially those who live in circumstances that limit their interaction with nature, must have the opportunity to observe a variety of plants and animals in the classroom, on the school grounds, in the neighborhood, at home, in parks and streams and gardens, and at the zoo. But observing is not enough. The students should have reasons for their observations—reasons that prompt them to do something with the information they collect.

- *Some animals and plants are alike in the way they look and in the things they do, and others are very different from one another.*
- *Plants and animals have features that help them live in different environments.*
- *Stories sometimes give plants and animals attributes they really do not have.*
- *There is variation among individuals of one kind within a population.*
- *Offspring are very much, but not exactly alike, like their parents and like one another.*
- *Different plants and animals have external features that help them thrive in different kinds of places.*
- *Shapes such as circles, squares and triangles can be used to describe many things that can be seen.*

- *People are more likely to believe your ideas if you can give good reasons for them.*
- *Things in nature and things people make have very different sizes, weights, ages, and speeds.*
- *Describe and compare things in terms of number, shape, texture, size, weight, color, and motion.*
- *Draw pictures that correctly portray at least some features of the thing being described.*

NRC Standards
- *Each plant or animal has different structures that serve different functions in growth, survival, and reproduction. For example, humans have distinct body structures for walking, holding, seeing, and talking.*
- *Many characteristics of an organism are inherited from the parents of the organism, but other characteristics result from an individual's interactions with the environment. Inherited characteristics include the color of flowers and the number of limbs of an animal. Other features, such as the ability to ride a bicycle, are learned through intereactions with the environment and cannot be passed on to the next generation.*

NCTM Standards 2000*
- *Count with understanding and recognize "how many" in sets of objects*
- *Develop understanding of the relative position and magnitude of whole numbers and of ordinal and cardinal numbers and their connections*
- *Connect number words and numerals to the quantities they represent, using various physical models and representations*
- *Compare and order objects according to the attributes of length, volume, weight, area, and time*
- *Understand how to measure using nonstandard and standard units*
- *Measure with multiple copies of units of the same size, such as paper clips laid end to end*
- *Use tools to measure*

Science
Life science
    characteristics of organisms
    organisms and environments

Integrated Processes
Observing
Communicating
Comparing and contrasting

Materials
It Must Be a Bird (Big Book)
KWL chart(s)
A real bird, if possible, or assorted bird pictures showing legs and feet

Procedure
Total Group Activity—Teacher Directed
1. Review the KWL chart and what the children have observed and learned about birds.
2. Read (and sing!) the big book *It Must Be A Bird*.
3. Use individual cards to review each bird characteristic and compare the information to the visiting bird or bird pictures.
4. Have students compare the real bird to a picture and place an X in **yes** or **no** row in the chart (see below). Or draw a picture of visiting bird's part in the correct box (e.g., feathers—same color, pattern, shape). If appropriate ask, "How do you know?"
5. Ask children to sketch the visiting bird with pencil. Encourage a drawing "as big as the bird." Add color with watercolor or craypas. (This will maintain the pencil sketch while marker and crayon may obscure details.) Keep and date for child's portfolio.

Extensions
1. If you have another type of bird visit your classroom, do a comparative chart with Bird 1 and Bird 2 (for yes or no).

Bird 1's Name	Feathers	Tail	Eyes on side	Feet: perch and climb	Legs: scales and claws	Flies
Yes 😊						
No ☹						

2. Use *Environment Cards* (provided in this curriculum). Make two copies on card stock. Color and laminate. Leave one set intact. Cut name labels from second set. Have children match picture and label.

Room Display
In Writing and Art areas, display individual cards with bird characteristics clearly labeled. Provide bird picture (see *Tissue Paper Bird* in *Resource* section) and tracing paper or 9" x 12" white tissue pieces and pencils for children to trace the diagram. If appropriate have children add names of parts as well. **NOTE:** Two clothespins at top of diagram will hold tissue in place while tracing with pencils. Remove tissue for coloring with crayons.

*   Reprinted with permission from *Principles and Standards for School Mathematics,* 2000 by the National Council of Teachers of Mathematics. All rights reserved.

Feet Task Cards

Topic
Types of bird feet

Key Question
Why do different birds have different types of feet?

Focus
The students will explore different types of bird feet.

Guiding Documents
Project 2061 Benchmarks
- People can often learn about things around them by just observing those things carefully, but sometimes they can learn more by doing something to the things and noting what happens.
- Describing things as accurately as possible is important in science because it enables people to compare their observations with those of others.
- When trying to build something or to get something to work better, it usually helps to follow directions if there are any or to ask someone who has done it before for suggestions.
- People are more likely to believe your ideas if you can give good reasons for them.
- Describe and compare things in terms of number, shape, texture, size, weight, color, and motion.
- Draw pictures that correctly portray at least some features of the thing being described.

NRC Standards
- Scientists use different kinds of investigations depending on the questions they are trying to answer. Types of investigations include describing objects, events, and organisms; classifying them; and doing a fair test (experimenting).
- Organisms have basic needs. For example, animals need air, water, and food; plants require air, water, nutrients, and light. Organisms can survive only in environments in which their needs can be met.
- Each plant or animal has different structures that serve different functions in growth, survival, and reproduction.

NCTM Standards 2000*
- Connect number words and numerals to the quantities they represent, using various physical models and representations
- Understand how to measure using nonstandard and standard units
- Measure with multiple copies of units of the same size, such as paper clips laid end to end
- Use tools to measure

Science
Life science
    characteristics of organisms
    organisms and environments

Math
Measuring
Counting

Integrated Processes
Observing
Communicating
Comparing and contrasting
Classifying

Materials (see Individual *Task Cards*)
Craft sticks
Paper fasteners
Crayons
Markers
Butcher paper
Rubber bands, large and small
Empty aquarium
Blocks
Styrofoam meat trays
Latex gloves
Twist ties or pipe cleaners
Assorted cylinders
String
Unifix cubes
Clear plastic lids
Hot glue gun and glue
Sand tray
Lunch sacks
Newspaper
Stapler
Hole punch
Craft foam sheets
Manila paper
Construction paper
Stamp pad
Transparency sheets
File folder
Clasp envelope

Management
1. You may
   • Run these task cards on colored tag board to code them for different tasks (i.e., all *feet* experiences one color or all *math* same color). Laminate and fold in half so that student side is showing in centers, **or**
   • Duplicate and mount on file folder or large index card. (Student directions on one side and teacher directions on the other.) Color and laminate.
2. The cards are intended for learning stations.
3. Introduce one task at a time.
4. Demonstrate the directions printed on the card for the children.
5. If there is a drawing or written response expected, model that also. If a model is made, leave yours at the station so children may refer to it.
6. If interest remains high at this station, leave it for the children when you add the next station. Stations may be set up on a special table or on a cookie sheet or serving tray placed in an out-of-the-way place in your classroom, preferably near a window.
7. Note: In the set of *Task Cards,* there are *Teacher Cards* that do not have an accompanying *Student Card.* These consist of centers or games that you can set up for the children and only require verbal directions from the teacher.

*   Reprinted with permission from *Principles and Standards for School Mathematics,* 2000 by the National Council of Teachers of Mathematics. All rights reserved.

Crafty Feet

Skills
Observing
Comparing and contrasting
Applying
Communicating
Working cooperatively

Materials
3 jumbo craft sticks (tongue depressors)
1 paper fastener
Crayons
2 small rubber bands
2 large rubber bands
Large empty aquarium

Background Information
Things move in different ways. External features determine environments in which birds live.

Directions
- Use an awl or protractor to make a small hole in one end of the craft sticks. To keep the wood from splitting, put a piece of strapping tape or book binking tape over the end of the sticks before making the hole.
- Number the sticks with permanent marker—1, 2, 3.
- Stack the sticks, aligning the holes, with stick 3 on top, 2 in the middle, and 1 on the bottom.
- Insert the paper fastener through the stick labeled 3.
- Add large rubber bands (one band over sticks 1 and 2 and one band over sticks 2 and 3).
- Have children work in pairs to put on bands and experiment with the tension of the "tendon bands" of the perching bird feet. Ask "What happens when you pull stick 1 and 3 at the same time?" "What do you feel?"
- Change to small rubber bands and repeat.

Safety Measure—Place aquarium on its side. Have children work inside aquarium to safeguard against shooting bands!

Feet—Science, Art, Paired Activity • Activity 1—Teacher Card

- ✂

Crafty Feet

1. Work with a friend.
2. Put one large rubber band over sticks 1 and 2 and another large rubber band over sticks 2 and 3.
3. Put sticks into aquarium.
4. Now pull sticks 1 and 3. What happens to stick 2?
5. Change the bands to small rubber bands and try again. What do you notice happens to stick 2?
6. How does the size of the bands change what happens to the sticks?
7. Draw or write what you see.

Feet • Activity 1—Student Card

Rubber Band Tendons

Skills
Observing
Comparing and contrasting
Applying

Materials
3 rubber bands, small enough that they create tension on child's fingers when hand is partially closed
Blocks

Background Information
This activity simulates birds' perching feet.

Directions
- Demonstrate the procedure for children before having them do the investigation.
- Have the first child hold the block in one hand.
- Direct the second child to connect the three rubber bands to the first child's hand that is holding the block in the following way: one to connect the thumb to the forefinger, one to connect the forefinger to the middle finger, and one to connect the middle finger to the ring finger.
- Ask the first child to release the block by stretching the rubber bands.
- Have children change roles and repeat.

Feet—Science, Paired Activity • Activity 2—Teacher Card

- ✂

Rubber Band Tendons

1. Use 3 and 1 .

2. Put the in one of your hands.

3. Ask a friend to help you put the 3  from your thumb to your pointer, from your pointer to your tall man, and your tall man and your ring man.

4. Stretch your fingers out to let go of the .

Feet • Activity 2—Student Card

Bird Tracking

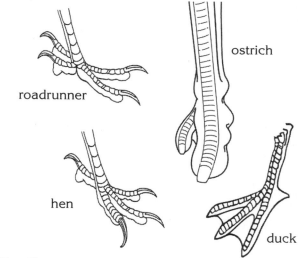

roadrunner

hen

ostrich

duck

Skills
Skills
Observing
Comparing and contrasting
Drawing conclusions

Materials
Styrofoam meat trays (with sides removed to make flat piece)
Crayons
Paper
Pictures of a duck, a hen, an owl, an ostrich, and a roadrunner

Preparation
• Read or have available *Animal Footnotes* by Q.L. Pearce (Silver Press, 1991).
• Use pencil to outline the different types of bird feet onto the Styrofoam trays.
• Write the name of the appropriate bird on each tray.
• Make rubbings of each of the different types of bird feet.
• In another area, place the rubbing sample next to a picture of that bird.

Feet—Science, Art • Activity 3—Teacher Card

Directions
• Have child place a sheet of paper over a tray track and use a crayon to make a rubbing of the track and bird's name.
• Direct the child to take the paper to the other area and draw a picture of bird that made this track.

Bird Tracking

1. Choose one track tray.
2. Place paper on top of the tray.
3. Rub a crayon over the tray until you can see the track and the bird's name.
4. Find which bird made this track by matching the bird's name to its picture.
5. Make your own picture next to your track.

Feet • Activity 3—Student Card

Feel Like Feet

Skills
Observing
Communicating
Comparing and contrasting
Estimating
Measuring

Materials
Latex gloves
Twist ties (or pipe cleaners)
Assorted cylinders or branches
String
Unifix cubes
Paper or journal
Pencil

Directions
- Prepare latex gloves by turning "pinkie" fingers to inside of gloves and closing them off with a twist tie. Students will then slip their hands into the gloves to simulate a bird that has three forward "toes" and one back "toe." (If you use yellow gloves, you can call these "finch feet.")
- Provide a variety of branches or cylindrical blocks on which students can practice "perching." Let child decide which branch feels "just right."
- Direct students to remove the gloves.
- Have students pair up to determine the circumference measurement of their chosen branch or block. The two should wrap a string around the branch or block and cut the string to equal the circumference.
- Have them lay the string out straight and estimate its length in Unifix cubes.
- Direct them to record their estimate on paper or in a journal.
- Allow time for students to connect cubes along the length of string and compare their estimate with the actual length.

Feet—Math • Activity 4—Teacher Card

Feel Like Feet

1. Put on gloves.
2. Use the branches to land on with your perching feet—three "toes" forward and one "toe" back.
3. Choose one branch that feels "just right."
4. Remove your gloves. Ask a friend to help you cut a string that will go around your branch.
5. Record how many cubes long you think your string will be.
6. Lay your string out straight and snap together cubes to match the string.
7. Compare your results with your estimate.

Complete this statement:

My string was _____ cubes (longer/ shorter) than my cube estimate.

Now try this:

Estimate using another branch. Write a < and > statement to compare lengths of the two strings.

Finish this statement:

My first string was _____ than my second string.

Feet • Activity 4—Student Card

Splash Like a Duck   Scratch Like a Hen

Skills
Observing
Comparing and contrasting
Applying

Materials
4 clear lids from 3 lb. coffee cans or shortening containers
6 craft sticks
Hot glue
Sand tray or table
Water basin or table
Paper or journal

Preparation
Make Duck Feet
- Cut "duck" feet from two lids.
- Hot glue three craft stick "toes" to one foot.
- Hot glue two feet together, sealing their edges.

Make Hen Feet
- Cut "hen" feet from two lids.
- Hot glue three craft stick "toes" to one foot.
- Hot glue two feet together, sealing the edges.

Directions
- Use with sand tray (or table) and water basin (or table).
- Ask child to predict which feet will work best in which "habitat." Ask them, "How do you know?"

Feet—Science, Art • Activity 5—Teacher Card

Splash Like a Duck   Scratch Like a Hen

1. Try the duck's foot and the hen's foot to find out:

   Which foot works best in a water habitat?

   Which foot works best in a sandy habitat?

2. Draw what happened in your journal.

Feet • Activity 5—Student Card

Bird Feet in a Bag

Skills
Observing
Applying

Materials
Lunch sacks
Stapler
String
Markers
Newspaper strips
Hole punch

2 front/2 back   two front   webbed   3 front/1 back

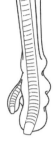

Background Information
Shape of feet is an adaptation to habitat and food acquisition.

Directions
- Have children choose a type of bird foot to create for themselves.
- Cut foot from the front open end of bag (cutting **both** sides). Leave top of bag uncut.

- Color yellow, black, gray, orange.
- Staple toes and **one** side of foot.
- Stuff with newspaper strips and staple last side closed.
- Hole punch top of the bag in two places and add string long enough to tie around child's ankle.
- The bird feet will rest on top of child's shoes.

Note:
Child will need to make a pair! Good way to make connection of bird having same number of feet as the child!

Feet—Science, Art • Activity 6—Teacher Card

Bird Feet in a Bag

1. Draw **one** of these feet on the bag.

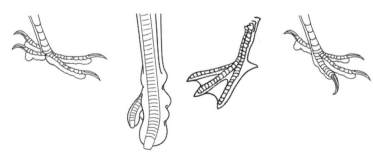

2. Leave bag closed. Cut out foot.
3. Do the **same** foot with a second bag. (**Birds** and **you** need **2** feet).
4. Color foot **yellow, black, gray** or **orange.**
5. Staple all but one side closed.
6. Stuff with newspaper strips.
7. Staple last side closed.

8. Punch **two** holes at top of foot.
9. Put string through holes and tie to ankle. You are now a bird!

Feet • Activity 6—Student Card

Where Am I Going?

Skills
Observing
Comparing and contrasting
Drawing conclusions

Materials
Fun foam, wood block, and hot glue
12" x 18" manila paper, cut in half
Stamp pad
Markers

Preparation
- Prior to setting up the station, cut feet stamps from fun foam. Hot glue foam to a wood block.

road runner, woodpecker   duck, goose

ostrich   rooster

- Mark a small x on the upper left corner of the 6" x 18" paper and a small ● on the upper right corner.

Directions
- Have children choose one bird track stamp and use stamp pad to make tracks across paper (from left to right, from x to o) in a trail.
- Have them add the appropriate habitat details to picture.
- At the right edge of the paper, the o side, direct them to draw that bird's picture in the habitat.
- Have the students fold over the right side of the paper, the o side, just enough to cover bird's picture.
- Write "Where Am I Going?" on the flap.
- Open up the paper and above the bird's picture write the name of the habitat.

Extensions
- Read *Rosie's Walk* by Pat Hutchins (Scholastic, Inc. New York. 1987). Tell children, "Imagine a predator for your bird. Where could your bird walk and what things could happen to your predator on the way? Make bird tracks across the pages of your book." (Children may write their story or dictate it. See *Literary Link* for *Rosie Shapes Up*, Activity 8.)
- *Hattie and the Fox* by Mem Fox (Aladdin Books. New York. 1986). Compare and contrast with a Venn Diagram how the books are alike and different.

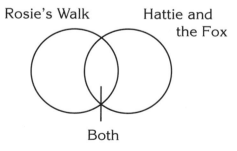

Feet—Science, Literary Link • Activity 7—Teacher Card

Where Am I Going?

1. Choose a bird track stamp.
2. Starting at the x side, walk your bird across your paper.
3. Draw things your bird might see along the way.
4. On the ● side, draw your bird that made that track.
5. Fold the ● side over to hide your bird picture.
6. Write "Where Am I Going?" on the flap.
7. Draw some more of your picture that would hide your bird (colors, patterns of leaves, and so on).

Want to do more?
Make an animal that might want to eat your bird. "Hide" it somewhere in your picture! Write a story **or** tell your story to a friend **or** let your teacher write down your story.

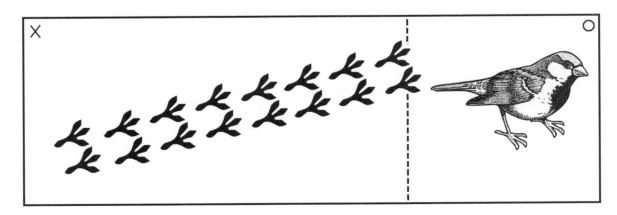

Rosie Shapes Up!

Skills
Observing
Communicating
Shapes integration; geometric shapes in the environment using positional words

Materials
Shape templates
Large butcher paper
Markers

Preparation
- Use squares, circles, triangles, and rectangles.
- Provide templates for these shapes (include various sizes) or have children cut their own.

Directions
- Use large butcher paper strips and add details (as children create them in the sequence of the story).
- Make into a classroom mural or walk-on story.
- For retelling, children can walk **on** the story if it is on the floor or they can walk along the wall if posted as a mural.

For literature link: add to each detail the appropriate positional words: **across, around, over, past, through, under**. (These are critical math understanding words.)

Extensions
- Set up an obstacle course in your classroom (or playground) and have children move through areas **while** saying what they're doing. ("I'm going across the table." "I'm going around the chair.")
- Have headbands or puppets available in a drama center to reenact the story.
  - Provide plastic hen and fox to block center and encourage obstacle course mazes for animals. (Take pictures of completed block mazes with children that have constructed them for display in classroom.)

Story Scenes

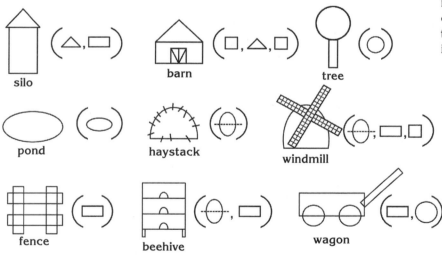

silo   barn   tree

pond   haystack   windmill

fence   beehive   wagon

Shapes Needed

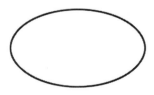

Overhead Story Theater

(based on *Rosie's Walk* by Pat Hutchins)

Skills
Observing
Communicating
Using ordinal vocabulary

Materials
2 transparency sheets
File folder
Clasp envelope, $6\frac{1}{2}$" x $9\frac{1}{2}$"
Permanent markers

Preparation
1. Overhead Story Theater: Use a regular file folder and cut out a window from one side of the folder. Tape a transparency sheet behind the opening. Draw an outdoor scene on the transparency sheet with permanent pens. On the other side of the folder, tape the clasp envelope for the storage of the story parts.
2. Use permanent marking pens to draw Rosie, Fox and story scenes on 3" x 3" squares of transparency plastic. Place the story parts in the envelope.

Directions
Place the file folder scene on the overhead projector and have two children retell the story while placing figures on the overhead. (A third child can read the story from the book.)
Note: Reinforce ordinal vocabulary—first, silo; second, pond; third, haystack; etc.

Feet—Math, Literature • Activity 9—Teacher Resource Card

Story Bag

(based on *Rosie's Walk* by Pat Hutchins)

Skills
Observing
Communicating
Sequencing
Using ordinal vocabulary

Materials
Lunch sacks or plain grocery bags
Construction paper, optional
Scissors, optional
Glue
Craft sticks
Markers

Directions
- Have children draw scenes (in order) from the story on the outside of the bag. Older children can draw and cut scenes from different colors of construction paper and glue them to the outside of the bag.
- Have students make two craft stick puppets, Rosie and Fox, to go with the bag. (The puppets can be stored in the bag.)

Note: Encourage and reinforce children using positional and ordinal vocabulary when retelling the story.

Feet—Math, Art, Literature • Activity 10—Teacher Card

Story Bag

1. Draw the different parts of the story **in order** on the outside of your bag or use construction paper to cut out parts and glue on the bag.
2. Draw or cut out construction paper parts for Roxie and Fox. Glue them onto the craft sticks to make puppets.
3. Tell the story to a friend.
4. Put your puppets in your story bag.

Feet • Activity 10—Student Card

A Foxy Tale of a Tail!
(based on *Hattie and the Fox* by Mem Fox)

Skills
Observing
Communicating
Sequencing
Counting

Materials
Paper
Markers

Directions
1. Children will create a layered book. The layers will include:
   a. nose
   b. nose and two eyes
   c. nose, two eyes, and two ears
   d. nose, two eyes, two ears, and four legs
   e. nose, two eyes, two ears, four legs, and a body
   f. nose, two eyes, two ears, four legs, a body, and a tail!
   g. Last page write, "It's a fox!"

Variation
Change the habitat—type of bird and likely predator

Extensions
1. *Hattie and the Fox* makes a wonderful Reader's Theater. Assign speaking parts to the following: Hattie, Goose, Pig, Sheep, Horse, Cow, Narrator (to describe action). Children can create head bands for their animals and while the narrator reads the connective text from the book, children say their lines and provide the appropriate action.
2. Provide puppets (or have children construct them from paper bags) for a drama center to retell the story.
3. Provide small animals from the story and small trees and bushes (made by the children from toilet paper rolls) and set up environments (in the block center or sand table).

Hattie and the Fox and Rosie's Walk
Ideas for Expanding the Literature

Math
Addition
Graphing
Geometric shapes

Skills
Observing
Comparing and contrasting
Geometry

Hattie and the Fox
Add up the parts show
    1 nose + 0 = 1 part
    1 nose + 2 eyes = 3 parts
    1 nose + 2 eyes + 2 ears = 5 parts

Rosie's Walk
Add up and/or graph the shapes used in Rosie's walk. Numbers will vary depending on how many pages you use and the number of shapes identified.
    a. Use large sticky notes and tally the shapes and number of shapes for each page. Place a sticky note on that page.
    b. When finished looking at the book, remove the sticky notes from the pages and construct a graph with the total group.

Extension
Have children repeat process in paired groups. Compare the findings.

Feet—Math, Science, Literature • Activity 11—Teacher Resource Card

Eggs and Nests

Which Came First, the Egg or the Nest?

The life cycle of the bird begins in an egg contained inside a hard shell made of **calcium**. The egg consists of three main parts: the **yolk** (which contains food for the growing chick), the **albumen** (the white, which constitutes two-thirds of the egg's weight and provides protein, water, and a bacterial fighter to protect against any bacteria that makes its way through the shell), and the **chalaza** (which looks like white twists attached to the yolk and protects the yolk in a developing chick from being jarred).

Eggshells are full of **air holes** that can be seen with a magnifying glass. The dome shape makes the egg extremely strong. The egg must support the weight of the adult bird. Empty ostrich eggs are so strong they are used by African tribesmen as canteens to carry water. The size of the egg varies with the size of the bird—from the smallest hummingbird egg to the largest ostrich egg. If you compare the weight of the egg to its mother, the England Kiwi weighs only four times more than her egg while the hummingbird weighs eight times more and the ostrich 50 times more.

The colors, patterns, and shapes of the eggs vary according to the habitat and location of the nest. Colors vary from white (for birds that have protected nests—like owls) to the emu egg that starts out green and turns to a shiny black. **Camouflaged** eggs protect eggs from hungry predators when these are laid in more open areas. Shapes vary from the round owl egg to the pointed murre (sea bird) egg that keeps it from rolling off its rocky ledge home. (See the Eyewitness Book by David Burnie, *Bird*—Alfred A. Knopf Co. New York. 1988—for a wonderful set of egg pictures that show various sizes, colors, shapes, and patterns in relation to each other.) The number of eggs laid also varies from a single egg laid by the albatross to chickens that will continue to lays eggs as their eggs are removed by the farmer.

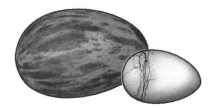

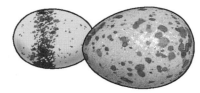

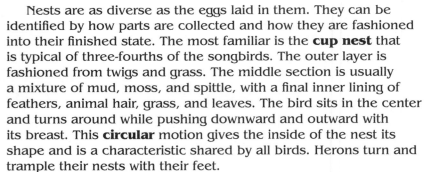

Nests are as diverse as the eggs laid in them. They can be identified by how parts are collected and how they are fashioned into their finished state. The most familiar is the **cup nest** that is typical of three-fourths of the songbirds. The outer layer is fashioned from twigs and grass. The middle section is usually a mixture of mud, moss, and spittle, with a final inner lining of feathers, animal hair, grass, and leaves. The bird sits in the center and turns around while pushing downward and outward with its breast. This **circular** motion gives the inside of the nest its shape and is a characteristic shared by all birds. Herons turn and trample their nests with their feet.

Natural materials, such as feathers, seed heads, spider webs, and animal hair support and insulate the nest. Feathers may be collected from other birds or they may use their own. Sparrows pull feathers from the backs of larger birds while waterfowl use their own feathers. **Manufactured** fibers such as string, aluminum foil, and plastic bags are also incorporated into the nest.

Unusual nests include the baglike nest of the Baltimore Oriole made from string and animal hair and the weaver bird's trumpet-shaped nest constructed with knots tied by the bird with its beak and feet. Oven birds build a two room adobe glove that looks like a baking oven. Hawks and starlings use green leaves that are regularly replenished. The horned coot builds an island of rocks that it carries in its mouth from nearby mountains before it creates its nest among the water plants. Lazy birds, like the cuckoo and cowbird, sneak their eggs into other birds' nests. Sea birds do the minimum for their nests, laying their eggs on bare rocks or shallow holes in the sand.

Owls are the poorest builders since their nests, which are made of piles of sticks, sometimes fall apart. Owls are probably the most diverse nesters. Some raise their young in hollow trees, elf owls nest in holes in saguaro cacti, burrowing owls build underground, and the snowy owl nests in the cold ground of the tundra.

Eagle nests can be 10 feet across and 10 feet deep. Nests are reused and added to year after year until the nest finally falls to the ground. An eagle's nest can weigh as much as two tons!

Nesting takes place in the tops of trees, in high branches, in low branches, bushes, hollow trees, or on ground level. Nesting also occurs in such places as the eaves and ledges of buildings.

Fancy feather displays, dances by courting males, and even presents of food are used by male birds to attract a female prior to the nest building. Most parents take care of their babies until they are able to fly and leave the nest.

To quote Edward Lear for *Book of Nonsense* (1846):

> There was an Old Man with a beard,
> Who said, "It is just as I feared —
> Two owls and a hen
> Four larks and a wren
> Have all built their nests in my beard!"

Egg and Nest Vocabulary

calcium	albumen
yolk	chalaza
hollow bones	air holes
dome shape	camouflage
cup nest	natural
manufactured	

Use this vocabulary in context. Provide word banks in the language area for creative writing. Add illustrations for the non-reader or emerging reader. Add definitions for the beginning reader.

Diagram of an Egg

Shell

Yolk

Chalaza

Albumen

Make Way for Ducklings
—by Robert McCloskey (1941, Scholastic, Inc.)

This account of a pair of ducks raising their babies in Boston is filled with correct facts as well as being an entertaining story that is a classic in children's literature.

Math
Graphing
Problem solving

Literature Link

Background Information
This is based on a true story of an event that was reported in the Boston papers. There is a video available from Discovery Collector's Edition called *A Little Duck Tale* about another duck family in downtown Tokyo. It is about a real-life duckling name Chibi and is available from the Discovery Channel (800-222-6105) or the Nature Company (800-227-1114). The video is 55 minutes long, and you may want to divide it into sections and compare and contrast the story with *Make Way for Ducklings* with a Venn Diagram.

Procedure
Part One
1. Tell the story twice, once for an overview and to just enjoy the narrative and illustrations. The second time stop and write down on a chart facts about nest-making and duckling-raising that can later be determined to be realistic or fictional. (See "How Can We Best Use Children's Literature in Teaching Science Concepts?" *Science and Children.* March 1995. pp. 16-19, 43.)

Part Two
1. One of the ways to use this book is as a math story problem-solving device. Duplicate enough cutouts so that each child has eight ducklings and one mother duck. Place each child's set in a resealable plastic bag. (You may want to code the duckling sets on the back of each cutout using color dots so that they can be easily sorted into sets.) Make a set for yourself, coloring the eight ducklings yellow and leaving the mother duck white. Laminate your set for extended use.
2. Talk with the children about the ways the ducklings could get separated from the parents.

Use these ideas to make up stories problems for the children to act out with their story boards. (For example: "Two ducklings got lost when they walked through the park." The child removes two cutouts from the board. "How many ducklings are still following Mrs. Mallard?"

Part Three
1. Instruct the children to draw their own story about what might happen to the eight ducklings. Have them write (or dictate) their story to go with their pictures. (Use as a bulletin board and/or make into a class book.) *Posing Open-Ended Questions* (1995) by Christine Myren, available from Teaching Resource Center (800-833-3389) has a "Levels of Understanding" continuum to follow with the story that will assist you in gauging your student's math story ability for Grades K-2.

Extension
If the child uses numbers with understanding in his/her story, encourage writing the number sentence to go with the story. For more mature students, a series of "Duck Adventures" could be constructed around the various possibilities this book suggests.

Note: The swan boats still cruise around the Public Garden of Boston, and there are brass duck and duckling statues that are child-sized for children to climb and count!

Story Board Cutouts

Introductory Activity
—Eggs and Nests

Focus
Students will compare and contrast different bird eggs and nest types

Key Question
Where and how do birds begin?

Guiding Documents
Project 2061 Benchmarks
- People can often learn about things around them by just observing those things carefully, but sometimes they can learn more by doing something to the things and noting what happens.
- Tools such as thermometers, magnifiers, rulers or balances often give more information about things than can be obtained by just observing things without their help.
- Describing things as accurately as possible is important in science because it enables people to compare their observations with those of others.
- When people give different descriptions of the same thing, it is usually a good idea to make some fresh observations instead of just arguing about who is right.
- Everybody can do science and invent things and ideas.
- In doing science, it is often helpful to work with a team and to share findings with others. All team members should reach their own individual conclusions, however, about what the findings mean.
- A lot can be learned about plants and animals by observing them closely, but care must be taken to know the needs of living things and how to provide for them in the classroom.
- Some animals and plants are alike in the way they look and in the things they do, and others are very different from one another.
- Plants and animals have features that help them live in different environments.
- Stories sometimes give plants and animals attributes they really do not have.
- There is a variation among individuals on one kind within a population.
- Offspring are very much, but not exactly, like their parents and like one another.
- Magnifiers help people see things they could not see without them.

- Most living things need water, food, and air.
- Different plants and animals have external features that help them thrive in different kinds of places.

NRC Standard
- Plants and animals have life cycles that include being born, developing into adults, reproducing, and eventually dying. The details of this life cycle are different for different organisms.

NCTM Standards 2000*
- Count with understanding and recognize "how many" in sets of objects
- Represent data using concrete objects, pictures, and graphs

Science
Life science
  characteristics of organisms
  organisms and environments

Integrated Processes
Observing
Communicating

Materials
Butcher paper or chart paper or poster board
Sticky notes
Permanent pens, different colors

Background Information
Teacher information: Ducklings will follow any large moving object as if it were their parent. This is called *imprinting*. They follow their real mother in a row.

Literary Link
Molleson, Diane. *How Ducklings Grow.* Scholastic, Inc. New York. 1993.

Procedure
Part One

1. Sing and act out "Five Little Ducks" with children (see *Bird Feet* section).

Part Two
1. Tell the children to imagine that they are one of those little ducks.

   "Close your eyes and make yourself small enough to fit into a duck egg. Curl up on the floor as small as you can. Smaller! Tighter! It's so tight inside your shell you cannot move at all. You want to get out and stretch so you put your duck beak up close to the end of the shell where there's a little air and you quack softly to your mother that it's time to come out of your shell. Can you do that now? Very softly.

   "Now feel your nose. Imagine a tooth right on the end of your nose. It's a special tooth that will break open the shell. It's called an **egg tooth**. Can you feel it? Use that special egg tooth and start to twist and turn and move your head to crack open the shell. Hooray! There's a tiny crack on your shell. That was hard work! You'd better rest for a minute.

   "Now move your head again and make the crack bigger. Turn your body so you can crack the shell on the other side. This is hard work. Let's rest a minute. Are you ready? Twist some more and break away the rest of the shell so you can wiggle out of the shell and onto the ground. Baby ducklings, you are worn out! You can hardly lift your head. You try to hold it up, but down it goes while you rest some more.

   "Now you feel the feathers on your wings drying. See if you can lift your wing. Great! Try the other wing. Can you lift that one, too? Wonderful! I think you're ready to try your legs. Remember, you're a duckling. Your feathers are still a little wet, but your eyes are open and you look around you and see your little brothers and sisters. Quack them a hello!"

Part Three: Brainstorming and Mapping
1. Ask, "When ducks are a year old they are ready to have ducklings of their own. What does a mother duck need to do to get ready for her ducklings?"
2. Using a large writing surface and different colored pens for each step in the process, encourage students to devise the "nest to duckling" story. Encourage dialog between students. Provide correct terminology where necessary.
3. Use different colored pens for each part of the mind map. (This can also be done in a circle with a pond in the center. (See *Literary Link* book as a guide.))

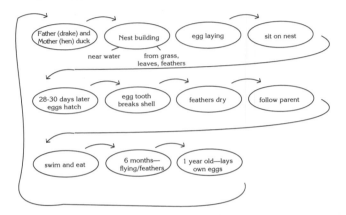

4. Ask children to pick a part of the mind map to illustrate. Write the child's name on a sticky note and place in on the part of the mind map that each is going to illustrate. Use the completed mind map as wall decoration.

Extension
Mount and laminate children's pictures. Use Velcro to attach to large mind map. Encourage children to remove and sequence pictures (on or off the mural) and retell the story.

Playground Activity
Provide duck head bands for four of the children. Create "families" of ducklings and let the children take turns being the mother duck and leading her babies around the playground.

*   Reprinted with permission from *Principles and Standards for School Mathematics,* 2000 by the National Council of Teachers of Mathematics. All rights reserved.

Eggs Task Cards
Eggs-am-ination Stations

Topic
Properties of eggs

Key Question
How do we sort and group eggs?

Focus
Students will note similarities and differences in eggs and group them accordingly.

Guiding Documents
Project 2061 Benchmarks
- *People can often learn about things around them by just observing those things carefully, but sometimes they can learn more by doing something to the things and noting what happens.*
- *Everybody can do science and invent things and ideas.*
- *When trying to build something or to get something to work better, it usually helps to follow directions if there are any or to ask someone who has done it before for suggestions.*
- *Things move in many different ways, such as straight, zigzag, round and round, back and forth, and fast and slow.*
- *Plants and animals have features that help them live in different environments.*
- *There is variation among individuals of one kind within a population.*
- *Offspring are very much, but not exactly alike, like their parents and like one another.*
- *Plants and animals both need to take in water, and animals need to take in food. In addition, plants need light.*
- *Different plants and animals have external features that help them thrive in different kinds of places.*
- *Simple graphs can help to tell about observations.*
- *Shapes such as circles, squares and triangles can be used to describe many things that can be seen.*
- *Things in nature and things people make have very different sizes, weights, ages, and speeds.*
- *Things in nature and things people make have very different sizes, weights, ages, and speeds.*
- *Make quantitative estimates of familiar lengths, weights, and time intervals and check them by measurements.*

NRC Standards
- *Organisms have basic needs. For example, animals need air, water, and food: plants require air, water, nutrients, and light. Organisms can survive only in environments in which their needs can be met. The world has many different environments, and distinct environments support the life of different types of organisms.*
- *Each plant or animal has different structures that serve different functions in growth, survival, and reproduction. For example, humans have distinct body structures for walking, holding, seeing, and talking.*
- *The behavior of individual organisms is influenced by internal cues (such as hunger) and by external cues (such as a change in the environment). Humans and other organisms have senses that help them detect internal and external cues.*

NCTM Standards 2000*
- *Count with understanding and recognize "how many" in sets of objects*
- *Recognize the attributes of length, volume, weight, area, and time*
- *Understand how to measure using nonstandard and standard units*
- *Measure with multiple copies of units of the same size, such as paper clips laid end to end*
- *Use tools to measure*
- *Develop strategies for estimating the perimeters, areas, and volumes of irregular shapes*
- *Represent data using concrete objects, pictures, and graphs*

Science
Life science
    characteristics of organisms
    organisms and environments

Integrated Processes
Observing
Communicating

Materials

Empty, clean egg shells
Masking tape
Scissors
String
9" paper plates
Bread slices
Electric fry pan
Biscuit cutter
Plastic bowls
2 large baby food jars
Balances
Large glass cup or bowl
Raw eggs
Boiled eggs
Empty egg cartons
Small trays or cookie sheets
Duck egg, quail egg, or other types
Task cards, for learning stations

Management

1. Run the task cards on colored tag to code them for different tasks (e.g., all *egg* experiences one color and all *math* another color). Laminate so that student side shows in the stations, or duplicate and mount the task cards on file folders or large index cards. Put student directions on one side and teacher directions on the other. Color and laminate.

3. Introduce one Task Card at a time. Demonstrate the directions printed on the card for the children. If there is a drawing or written response expected, demonstrate that also. Leave your example in the center for children to reference.

4. If interest remains high in a station, leave it for the children when you add the next station. Stations may be set up on a special table or on a cookie sheet or serving tray placed in an out-of-the-way place in your classroom, preferably near a window.

5. Note that there are *Teacher Resource Cards* that do not have an accompanying *Student Cards*. These consist of centers or games that can be set up for the children and only require verbal directions from the teacher.

6. Children will need their journals or *Eggs-am-in-ation* books.

* Reprinted with permission from *Principles and Standards for School Mathematics,* 2000 by the National Council of Teachers of Mathematics. All rights reserved.

Find My Mass

Skills
Observing
Comparing and contrasting
Estimating
Measuring
   mass
One-to-one correspondence

Materials
Balance
Unifix cubes and/or wooden cubes
Raw egg
Egg carton cups
Journal

Preparation
1. Cut apart egg carton into individual cups.
2. Write the child's name with permanent marker on the cup.

Directions
- Ask the child to make an estimation of how many cubes will be needed to balance his/her egg.
- Have the child put the egg in its cup in one pan of the balance and add cubes to the other pan until both pans equalize.
- Direct the child to count and record in the journal the actual number of cubes needed.

Extension
If you are able to get different bird eggs, use these as an extension and comparative experience.

Eggs—Mathematics • Activity 1—Teacher Card

Find My Mass

1. Place an egg in one side of the balance.
2. In your journal, write down how many cubes you think will be needed to balance the egg.
3. Add cubes, one at a time, until both pans are balanced.
4. Take out the cubes and count them. Write the number of the cubes in your journal.

Use heavier cubes. What will happen to your numbers now. Check your idea.

Eggs • Activity 1 • Student Card

String Me Around

Skills
Observing
Estimating
Measuring
    length
Comparing and contrasting

Materials
String
Scissors
3 column chart—too long,
    too short, just right
Masking tape
Unifix cubes
Journal
Egg

Directions
1. Invite a child to cut a length of string that he/she estimates will go around the largest part of the egg.
2. Ask two children to work together to hold and measure the egg using their estimated length.
3. Roll a piece of masking tape with sticky side out so that the children can attach their estimate string to the proper section of the chart.
4. Have them cut a second string to the actual length need to go around their egg.
5. Direct them to use Unifix cubes to measure the length of this string.

Too Long	Too Short	Just Right

Eggs—Mathematics • Activity 2—Teacher Card

String Me Around

1. Cut a piece of string you think will fit around your egg.
2. Ask a friend to hold your egg while you put the string around it. Place your string on the chart to show it is "too long," "too short," or "just right."
3. Cut another string that will go around your egg.

4. Glue this string in your journal.
5. Use Unifix cubes to measure your string. Be sure to snap the cubes together.

Finish this sentence: "My egg is _____ cubes around."

Eggs • Activity 2—Student Card

To Spin or Not To Spin!

Skills
Observing
Comparing and contrasting
Drawing conclusions

Materials
2 plates, one labeled "cooked" and one labeled "not cooked"
2 large baby food jars with labels removed
3 raw eggs, 1 in shell labeled "not cooked"
1 hard-boiled egg labeled "cooked"
Journal

Preparation
Scramble and microwave one egg in one of the baby food jars. Carefully crack the raw egg into the other jar. Label the jars with a permanent marker: "cooked" and "not cooked." Seal lids with 2-inch book binding tape. Use the permanent marker to label the hard-boiled egg.

Directions
- Direct child to spin the hard-boiled egg on the plate marked "cooked" and to spin the raw egg still in the shell on the plate marked "not cooked."
- Have her/him write in their journal which egg spun faster.
- Repeat the procedure with the baby food jars. Have the students observe what happens when the jars are tipped from side to side.

Eggs—Science • Activity 3—Teacher Card

- -

To Spin or Not To Spin!

1. Draw these plates and labels in your journal.
2. Spin the "cooked" egg. What do you notice? Write about it in your journal.
3. Spin the "not cooked" egg. What do you notice? Write about it in your journal.
4. Why do you think the eggs spin differently? Tell a friend.

1. Look at the two jars.
2. Move the jars back and forth. Do not shake!
3. Write in your journal (or tell a friend) about what you see.
4. Spin the two jars (one at a time) on the plates. What do you notice?
5. Finish this sentence: "If I were an egg and I were going to be in a spinning race, I would want to be _____ _____(cooked/not cooked) because

_____
_____."

Eggs • Activity 3—Student Card

Egg Diving

Skills
Observing
Measuring
    volume

Materials
Large glass cup or bowl
Water, color with food coloring
Masking tape, colored preferred
Spoon or egg dying metal holder

Preparation
Color water (blue, green, or red). Half-fill cup with water. Mark the water line with masking tape.

Directions
- Have child observe water level before and after lowering the egg.
- The terms "displacement" and "volume" are not necessary to use. Encourage terms like "higher," "halfway," "lower" in communicating observations.

Eggs—Science • Activity 4—Teacher Card

Egg Diving

1. Draw the "no egg" water picture in your journal.
2. Use the holder to place your egg carefully in the bowl. Draw your egg and the water picture again.
3. Write in your journal or tell a friend what happened to the water in the bowl.

> Try this in your bath tub with your own body. What happens to the water when you get it?

Eggs • Activity 4—Student Card

Float an Egg

Skills
Observing
Estimating
One-to-one correspondence

Materials
2 qt. glass bowl
Water
Salt in an open dish
Spoon for stirring
Dump pail
Cup measure
Water container with spoon
Journal
Raw egg in shell

Background Information
When salt is added to water, the salt water's density is greater than the plain water. The Dead Sea and the Great Salt Lake are very easy to float in because of the high salt concentration.

Directions
- Have the child place a raw egg still in the shell in a bowl and add two cups of water to the bowl.
- Direct the child to add salt, one teaspoon at a time, until the egg floats. (This will take about 10 teaspoons.)
- Have child remove the egg and dump the salty water so the station is ready for the next child.

Eggs—Science, Mathematics, Paired Activity • Activity 5—Teacher Card

Float an Egg

Work with a friend

1. Place your egg in the bowl.
2. Add 2 cups of water to the bowl.
3. Draw a picture of your egg in the bowl.
4. Add 1 spoon of salt to the water and stir gently. What happened to your egg? How many spoons of salt will it take to make the water salty enough to float your egg? Write that number guess in your journal next to your picture.
5. Add another spoonful of salt and stir. Ask your friend to tally the number of spoonfuls it takes until the egg floats. Write that in your journal.

6. Finish this sentence: "It took _____ spoons of salt before my egg floated. I guessed it would take _____ spoons."
7. When you are finished, please remove the egg and empty the salty water into the "dump pail" so that the station is ready for the next person.

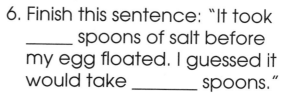

My guess was

_____

(too small, too large, just right).

Eggs • Activity 5—Student Card

Here's Looking at You!

Skills
Observing

Focus
Heat changes food

Materials
Electric fry pan with "hot" label
Aerosol cooking spray
Small bowls
Bread slices, 1 per child
Biscuit cutter
Soft butter or margarine
Popsicle sticks
Spatula
Plastic spoons
Salt and pepper
Journal

Preparation
Have the *Diagram of an Egg* page near the station with pencils and crayons available.

Directions
- This is a two-step station. First have the children crack their eggs into a bowl and draw what they see.
- Next, have them butter a piece of bread and cut out a hole in it using the biscuit cutter.
- Fry their egg in this "bread frame."
- Invite them to eat their egg.

Eggs—Science • Activity 6—Teacher Card

- -

Here's Looking at You!

1. Break your egg into the bowl. Draw what you see. Label the parts with their names. Color the picture.
2. Use the popsicle stick to butter one slice of bread.
3. Cut a circle out of the bread using the biscuit cutter. Give the bread frame to the teacher.
4. You teacher will help you slide your egg into the bread frame. (You may eat the cut out circle while your egg is cooking!)
5. Your teacher will cook your egg. What happens to your egg when it is cooked? Draw a picture in your journal.
6. Eat your egg!

Eggs • Activity 6—Student Card

Name Your Favorite

Skills
Observing
Graphing
Area
Perimeter

Materials
Hard-boiled eggs
Raw eggs
Chart paper
Assorted colored pens
Bowl
Paper plates
Mayonnaise
Teaspoon
Plastic spoons
Disposable bowls
Salt (in a small dish)
Sticky notes
Grouping circles and labels
Centimeter grid paper

Literature
There are several books that can be used with this activity:

1. *Eggbert, the Slightly Cracked Egg* by Tom Ross (G. P. Putnam's Sons. New York. 1994). This is a great book about being your own self, even if you look flawed to others. **Extension:** Have children use acrylic paints to paint their own plastic egg.

2. *The Most Wonderful Egg in the World* by Helme Heine (Aladdin Paperbacks. New York. 1987). This is about an egg-laying contest to prove that "what you can do is more important than what you look like." **Extension:** The most spectacular egg laid was square! Have children make square egg frame in a slice of bread and fry a square scrambled egg with food coloring added. Each child can scramble his/her own egg and add food coloring at the end and swirl it.

3. *The Great Big Especially Beautiful Easter Egg* by James Stevenson (Scholastic, Inc. New York. 1983). A grandparent tells an Easter egg story that will encourage beautiful egg dying experiences. **Extension:** Color hard-boiled eggs with some unusual colors. There are many on the market at Easter time. Or use natural dyes like purple onion skins (see directions at the end of this lesson). Design special egg baskets from strawberry baskets with curly ribbon to weave through holes and add plastic grass. Encourage children to give their creation to a favorite grandparent.

4. *Green Eggs and Ham* by Dr. Seuss (Beginner Books, Inc. New York. 1960). **Extension:** Chart children's responses before and after eating scrambled eggs with green food coloring added. (You can also add blue food coloring to show how blue and yellow mixed together make green!)

Before

Do you think you like green eggs and ham?

After

Did you like green eggs and ham?

5. *It Wasn't My Fault* by Helen Lester (Scholastic, Inc. New York. 1985). A bird lays an egg on Murdley Gurdson's head. As a clumsy child, Murdley led an unusually messed up life. This wonderful tale of a series of animals admitting their fault for an egg being laid on Murdley's head ends up with a scrambled egg part. This story follows *Green Eggs and Ham* in its scrambled happy ending. It lends itself to creative, innovative substitutions of other animals and circumstances for cause and effects and circular story writing.

Directions

1. Choose one or more of the suggested egg-related books and extensions to do earlier in the day or on the previous day.
2. Provide each child with a hard-boiled egg. Generate a word bank of their observations of the egg they are holding. Use chart paper and assorted colored pens. Write each response in a different color with a quick sketch if appropriate.

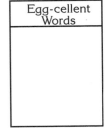

Egg-cellent Words

3. Say the rhyme "Humpty Dumpty." Ask the children to predict what would happen if you dropped an uncooked egg off the table into a bowl on the floor. After they have predicted the result, actually drop an egg into the bowl. Discuss what they see in the bowl and why it happened.
4. Pass a raw egg around the circle of children and have them hold it in the palm of their hand and squeeze it from end to end, not in the middle. An egg is very strong at the ends!

   Now ask each child to stand. Ask them to predict what will happen if they drop their hard-boiled eggs on the floor. Then actually have children drop their eggs! Invite them to compare their egg's shell to their friend's next to them. Use comparative terms—more cracked, less cracked.

   Give each child a paper plate. Have them write their names on the plates and place their eggs on them. Put the plates in the snack center. Two children will go to the center at a time so they can help each other.

Snack Center: Eggs, the Hard Way

Demonstrate how to "marble" a hard-boiled egg's shell by gently rolling it around and around and exerting gentle pressure on it. This way the shell will come off fairly easily and often in one piece. (Eggs that are boiled after they are one to two weeks old are easier to peel than eggs that are fresh.)

Remove the shell and save it on the plate. Cut the egg in half with a table knife, exposing the yolk. Provide mayonnaise, teaspoon, mixing spoon, and salt dish (to add a "pinch" of salt, and disposable bowls.

The children may create their own "egg-ceptional" egg snack:

Deviled Eggs—Mix yolk with a spoon of mayonnaise and one pinch of salt. Replace in the egg white. Eat.

Egg Boats—Eat egg as it is with a sprinkle of "sea salt."

Egg Salad—Cut up egg yolk and white. Add one spoon of mayonnaise and a pinch of salt. Eat.

Before leaving the snack center, have children write their names on sticky notes and place them on a Venn diagram.

I like my eggs _____.

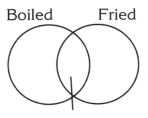

Boiled   Fried

Both Ways

Ways to Use Egg Shells

1. Use with centimeter grid paper. Ask children to predict how many squares a hard-boiled egg with the shell on will cover. Have them write that number at the side of the grid. Invite students to work in partners with one holding the egg while the second child draws around it. Direct them to color in the squares and count them. Have them write that number on the other side of the grid.

Shell On

I think ____ will be covered.

_____ squares were covered.

2. Have students do the same thing with the egg shell pieces. Ask them to compare the numbers and explain why there is a difference.

Shell Off

I think ____ will be covered.

_____ squares were covered.

3. Dye eggshells with egg dye or food color mixed with vinegar. Place the separate colors in zipper-type plastic bags. Have the students use the shells to create a mosaic picture.

Naturally Dyed Eggs

Ingredients
2 cups of water
Eggs
Onion skins, tea, or blueberries
Pan

Directions
1. Place the eggs in a pan with the water.
2. Add either onion skins, tea, or blueberries to the water with the eggs. Note: Yellow onion skins will color eggs yellow, purple onion skins will color eggs mauve, tea will color eggs brown, and blueberries will color the eggs blue.
3. Bring the water to a boil, then slow boil for at least 10 minutes.
4. Allow the eggs to sit in the water until they pick up the coloring of the water. Blueberries will take the longest for the color to set.

Variations
1. Try using red cabbage, carrot tops, and marigolds, or dandelions to dye the eggs.
2. Spinach eggs: Chop one pound fresh spinach into three-inch pieces. Add 4 cups of water and simmer for 1 hour. Remove the leaves. Add 4 teaspoons of white vinegar to spinach water. Add eggs and simmer for 30 minutes.

Eggs—Science • Activity 7—Teacher Card

Egg Droppers

Skills
Observing
Graphing
Measuring
   length
Relative numbers
Problem solving
Using tools
Creative writing

Directions
1. Determine several sites on the playground for the egg drop. Mark the sites with large-print numbers. Begin number at the lowest site and progress to the highest drop site. The children will drop their eggs at each site and check to see whether they broke. If they didn't, students will proceed to the next highest site and try again.
2. Ask parent volunteers with cameras to station themselves at various egg drop sites. Have them take pictures of children at each site where their egg finally broke.
3. Use these pictures to create a graph of where eggs were dropped and finally broken
4. Another graph might depict what kinds of materials children packed around their eggs. What was the most frequently used? ...most unusual?
5. For older students, use tape measures to measure heights of the different egg drop sites.

Extension
Use the pictures in a class book. Have students tell (or write) how they constructed their "egg droppers" and how many times (and where) their egg dropped before it broke.

Note
Be sure you have some extra eggs, plastic bags, cartons, and assorted packing materials for children who forget.

Dear Parents:

It's "Egg Time" in our room! We're going onto the playground with this one. Here's what we need you to do at home.

Use an empty half-gallon paper milk carton and one raw egg still in the shell. Place the egg in a resealable bag. With your child, decide what things around your house might protect the egg and keep it from breaking when it is dropped. Place these things in the milk carton, around the egg. Use masking tape to close the "egg carton." Remember, we need to be able to open the carton to check the egg, so use only masking tape. You may add anything to the inside of the carton to soften the crash. Nothing on the outside!

Write your child's name on the outside of the carton and send it to school

_____ (date).

We'll be dropping eggs during our playground time from various places on the playground. We'll be taking pictures, and you're welcome to join us at

_____ (time).

Thank you for your help.

Sincerely,

Domed Eggs

Skills
Observing
Weighing
Predicting
Shape structures
One-to-one correspondence

Materials
Empty egg shell halves from raw eggs
Masking tape
Scissors
5 books of various sizes
Bathroom scales, optional

Background Information
Eggs are dome shaped. This structure is commonly used in architecture because weight is evenly distributed down the sides of the dome. An egg must support the weight of an adult bird sitting on it.

Directions
- Place masking tape around the egg shell and trim with scissors so that it is even.
- Put four egg domes in a square touching each other.

Eggs—Science, Mathematics •Activity 7—Teacher Card

Domed Eggs

1. Place egg domes in a square. Draw this in your journal.
2. Predict what will happen when you put a book on the egg domes. Write it in your journal (or tell a friend).
3. Place a book on the domes. What happened?
4. How many books will your eggs hold?

Predict _____

Actual _____

Write these in your journal.

1. Weigh the books that your egg domes held. Write that weight in your journal.
2. Try the same experiment with three domes.

Eggs • Activity 7—Student Card

© 2004 AIMS Education Foundation

Secret Message

Skills
Observing
Change over time
Time
Experience story

Materials
Warm water
Glass bowl
Apple cider
Vinegar
Clear covered container
Raw eggs in shells
2 hard-boiled eggs
Magnifying glass
Stopwatch

Background Information
Egg shells are porous. These holes permit air to enter the shell so that the developing chick can breathe. Calcium makes up about half of the weight of the eggshell.

In *Part Two*, the bubbles are a result of carbon dioxide as the acid of the vinegar chemically reacts with the calcium of the shell. The reaction will leave the shell soft because the calcium will eventually dissolve. This can be observed in a short period (four hours), but is more dramatic overnight. The children can then handle this "rubbery" egg the next day. The secret message will stand out as the calcium is dissolved because the crayon wax has protected those parts of the shell from the vinegar. Be sure to have another hard-boiled egg to feel as a contrast.

Preparation
Use a white wax crayon to write a message on a boiled egg (e.g., "Let me out!")

Directions
Part One
1. Place one raw egg in a glass filled with warm water. Children will observe bubbles coming from eggs.
2. Set a stopwatch to time how long the bubbles continue to appear.
3. Have pairs of children continue to observe. Have them record their results in their journals and write times on sticky notes with both of their names. Chart results of the times.

Part Two
1. Place the hard-boiled egg with the secret message in a clear covered container. Cover the egg with vinegar.
2. Have children use magnifying glasses to observe the bubbles forming on the side of the egg.
3. Ask the children how these bubbles are different from those in the water and raw egg observation.

Extension
Record what the children say about their observations in a class experience story. This is a wonderful way to revisit a group experience. "First we …, then we …" and so on. Write their story on chart paper for retelling as a group. Duplicate the story, allowing space for their illustrations and send home to parents.

Eggs—Science, Mathematics, Literary Link • Activity 8—Teacher Card

Bones are Special

Skills
Observing
Comparing and contrasting

Materials
Clean chicken bones
Clean beef soup bone
Hammer
Heavy paper bag

Information
Bones of mammals are dense and thick while bird bones are thin and have holes. Bird bones are lighter. This is important when they fly and when they sit on their eggs.

Directions
- Children will place one of the chicken bones in the bag on the floor and hit it once with a hammer. They will open the bag and draw what they see.
- Have them do the same thing with the beef bone.

Eggs—Science, Mathematics • Activity 9—Teacher Card

Bones are Special

1. Place a chicken bone in the bag on the floor.
2. Hit it once with a hammer.
3. Open the bag. Draw what you see.

4. Put a beef bone in the bag on the floor.
5. Hit it once with a hammer.
6. Open the bag. Draw what you see.

Eggs • Activity 9—Student Card

Build a Bird

Skills
One-to-one correspondece
Classification
Symmetry

Materials
Large raw chicken
Butcher paper
Plate for bones
Bowl (for removed meat)
Soapy water and towels

Preparation
Boil a large chicken. (Cool in refrigerator until ready to use.) Draw an outline of the chicken on butcher paper.

Procedure
Part One
Children work in pairs and choose a part of the chicken to remove meat. Locate that part on the outline and place bones on the butcher wrap. Continue until all of the bones have been cleaned and placed on the outline. (Some children really enjoy this and some want no part of it. They all enjoy looking at the finished bone display!) Encourage children to note symmetry—leg bones on both sides, wings, etc. Discard the meat removed. It's been pretty well handled and is not sanitary enough to eat!

Part Two
Choose a large leg bone and place in a clear jar. Fill with cider vinegar. The next day, remove the bone and compare it to the other leg bone. The calcium will be removed with the vinegar and the bone will feel rubbery. Have children describe what they feel and chart their responses, or use a double Venn diagram.

How Are They Different		How Are They The Same	
vinegar bones	dry bones	vinegar bones	dry bones

or

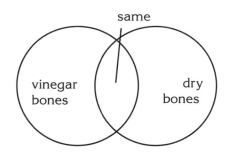

Part Three
Use cleaned bones from *Part One* and have children sort on chart.

wing	leg	back	ribs

Eggs—Science, Mathematics • Activity 10—Teacher Card

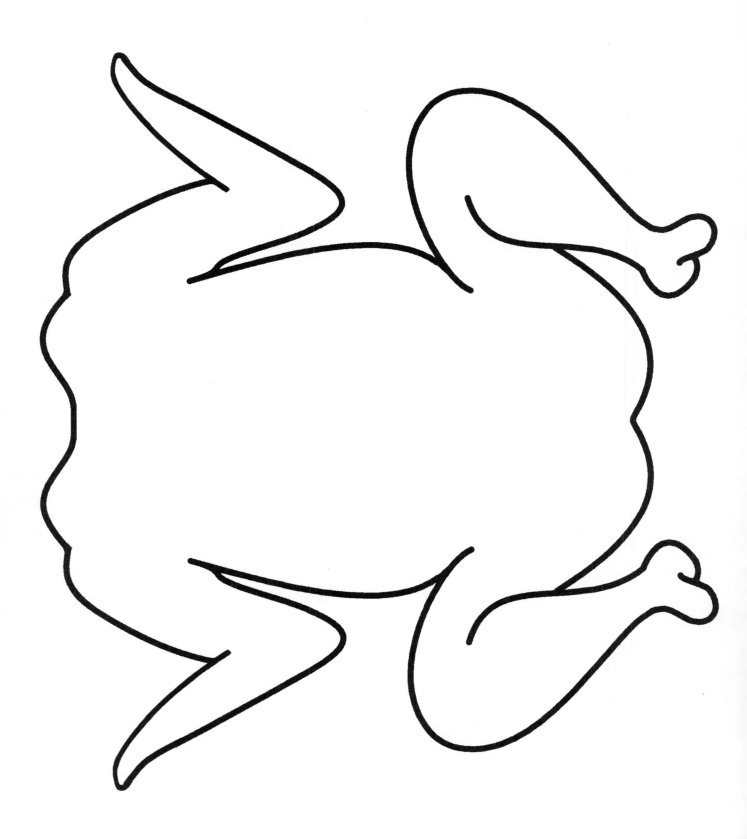

To Hatch or Not To Hatch!

Note to Teachers:

Hatching eggs is a common classroom experience using incubators and count down charts. Some naturalists that object to the practice of mechanically hatching eggs in a classroom. They contend that children are misled into thinking that these baby animals do not need parents and will miss the whole context of the reproductive, natural birth cycle. (For more information and suggested alternatives, write United Poultry Concerns, Inc. P.O. Box 59367, Potomac, Maryland 20859; (301) 948-2406.)

One viable alternative was outlined in *Science and Children* (May 1996), p. 26-28, "Henny Penny Goes To School" by Alida D. Frey. Ms. Frey tells about arranging with a breeder to have a brood hen come into her classroom where the children could observe first hand how a mother hen takes care of her eggs. The children were responsible for keeping the cage clean (because the pores in the eggs would clog with dirt). They still marked off the egg chart to "hatch day." Additional math and science activities were carried out as the expert breeder came in to "candle" the eggs and check the chick's growth. Ms. Frey cautions that some school districts have policies that prohibit such a project, so check with yours before you begin.

Build a Nest

Materials
Old bird nest
Cardboard cereal bowls
Assorted grasses and leaves, sticks (gather these in lunch bags on a nature walk to look for birds in the neighborhood by your school)
Mexican clay
Water
Small feathers

Procedure
Part One

If possible, examine and take apart an old bird nest. Call the children's attention to the circular pattern. Ask for children to give reasons for how this came to be.

Place the nesting materials on a chart for natural or human-made materials you find in the nest. (Save materials in a resealable plastic bag so children can repeat this exercise on their own later.)

Part Two

Provide bowls (as the base to build on). Children can use found natural materials to create their own nest. The clay, mixed with water and grass will hold the nest together. Press feathers into the clay as the last step.

Extension
Read *The Best Nest* by P.D. Eastman. Have the children create a story of where **they** would build their nest if they were a bird parent. Write on egg shape and place in dried nest.

Nesting Baskets

Skills
One-to-one counting
Graphing
Habitat

Materials
Berry baskets
Yarn
Cotton strings
Tinsel
Straw
Twigs
Pipe cleaners

Purpose
Children will create a bird's nest out of various materials to take home to hang on a tree near an outside window.

Directions
1. Have child fill berry basket with five of each of the following things: yarn, cotton strings, tinsel, straw, twigs.
2. Attach a handle with a pipe cleaner.
3. Duplicate and send home Parents' Note and child's basket.

Create an Egg

Note: Garlic press makes play dough into wonderful "grass-like" strings for creating "nesting materials" for these eggs. Squeeze play dough onto paper plate or into cardboard cereal bowl and add "eggs."

Extension
Have children create a trifold card for bird parent and habitat picture as backdrop for clay eggs.

Skills
One-to-one correspondence
Habitat

Materials
Colored play dough
Garlic press
Paper plates or bowls
Index cards
Construction paper
Colors

Directions
1. Provide various colored play dough and encourage egg making.
   Peacock lays 10 or more brownish eggs
   Bluebird lays 3 to 7 pale blue and white eggs
   Sea gull lays 1 to 4 grayish or greenish-brown spotted eggs
   Parrot lays round white eggs
   Eagle lays 2 white eggs
   Ostrich lays 10 almost round, dull yellow eggs
2. Have children label their eggs with index card containing bird's name and number of eggs. (Teacher can write this information on a sticky note for the child to copy onto index card.)
3. Use with poem:

I'm keeping them warm,
I'm as happy as can be;
My eggs will become
My little babies.
                                   –Donna VanderWeide

Egg Carton Math and Science

Skills
12 is a dozen
Weight
Sense of hearing to identify differences
The concept of a dozen as 12 can be reinforced in many ways using empty egg cartons.

Numbered Cups
Materials
Egg carton
Permanent marker
Counters (mini jelly beans or lima beans spray painted different colors)
Plastic eggs

Preparation
Use a permanent marker and number each section of the egg carton 1-12.
1. **One-to-One Correspondence; Reading Numbers; Quantities**—Use counters and place that many things in each carton section.
2. **Take and Shake**—Put one counter in egg carton and shake. Open and read the number where the counter landed. **Extension:** Use 2 counters and write a math sentence using the two numbers.
3. **Dotted Eggs**—Use plastic eggs with dot patterns 1-12. Have children count dots and place the egg in the correct carton cup. **Extension:** Separate plastic eggs and put dot pattern on both segments. Make sure eggs are all the same color! Children must put together halves that equal the numbers in the cups.

Unnumbered Cups
Materials
Egg carton
Plastic eggs
Small items to fit into eggs (i.e., rice, macaroni, marbles)
Tongs
Balance
Sand

1. **Egg Sounds**—In six of the eggs put sound items (i.e. rice, macaroni, block). Make a matching set of sound eggs with the other six eggs. Be sure eggs are either assorted colors that don't match sounds or are all one color. Children pick up one egg and shake. Then pick up another egg and shake. If the sounds are the same, they place them in the carton. If not, they try with another egg. **Note:** Young children tend to shake **both** eggs at the same time. Be sure to model the correct method!
2. **Tongs and Eggs**—(Wonderful small motor activity)—Have a bowl of colored eggs. Child uses tongs with his or her writing hand only and places eggs in carton while counting to 12.
3. **Assorted Colored Eggs**—Use for patterning. (Simplest pattern A-B-A-B or A-B-C)
4. **Assorted Sizes**—Seriate by size
5. **Assorted Weights**—Use the same size and color plastic egg. Fill with different amounts of sand. Seal eggs with hot glue gun or masking tape. Use balance to determine heaviest egg, next heaviest, etc.

Literary Links and Art

Egg-shaped Book

Start with two large oval shapes. Color one as a camouflaged egg shell (spots, streaks, colors). Cut it into two pieces with a zig-zag cut. Attach to uncut oval with a paper fastener. Draw a baby bird on the uncut oval. Use with poem:

I wonder how an egg's begun.
The yolk as yellow as the sun.
The color of the white is none.
You'd think the yolk and white would run
Before the shell was ever done.
But hen's don't lay a scrambled one!
—Autor Unknown

or

Ballad of a Boneless Chicken
from Jack Prelutsky's *New Kid on the Block*

Fold Out Egg Sequence Book

Fold an 8½" x 11" (or larger) paper into six sections. Cut out lower middle section. Refold by numbers. Draw sequence pictures of: • How Egg is Laid • Hatches • Is Cared for By Parents • Until it Can Fly

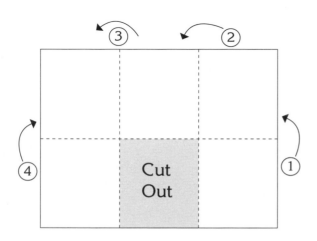

Fictional Egg Books

Choose one of these stories to read (or listen to a tape). What part(s) of the story could be true? Make up a book jacket cover for your book choice. Put "True Facts" from your book inside your book jacket. If the book is totally fiction, rewrite (or tell the story in a different way) to make it real.

Green Eggs and Ham by Dr. Seuss
The Best Nest by P.D. Eastman
Are You My Mother? by P.D. Eastman
Yertle the Turtle and Other Stories by Dr. Seuss
The Ugly Duckling
Horton Hatches an Egg by Dr. Seuss
The Great Big Especially Beautiful Easter Egg
     by James Stevenson
Golden Egg Book by Margaret Wise Brown
The Country Bunny and the Little Gold Shoes
     by Du Bose Heyward
Eggbert by Tom Ross
The Most Wonderful Egg in the World by Helme Heine

Dear Parents:

Your child has created a materials basket for the birds in your neighborhood to use in creating a nest.

Attach the basket to a tree near an outside window where you think birds might be attracted.

Any member of your family can participate in marking the chart but encourage your child to be in charge of checking the basket to see what's missing each day. (Even if they don't see a bird actually take an item, it's okay to color in the corresponding square.)

Return chart to school by _____ .

Thank you.

Sincerely,

What the birds used				
Yarn	Cotton	Tinsel	Straw	Twigs

Color in a space for each item the birds took

Feed-a-Bird Stations

Teacher Information

Approximately 82 million people in the United States actively feed wild birds. Only gardening is a more popular outdoor activity. Feeders provide birds with a reliable food source, regardless of the weather. It can also be an inducement to build a nest nearby.

The following centers will generate several types of bird feeders and bird feeding activities. Many tools and planning activities will generate measuring and math strategies.

Guiding Documents

Project Benchmarks
- *People can use objects and ways of doing things to solve problems.*
- *People may not be able to actually make or do everything that they can design. Design projects give students interesting opportunities to solve problems, use tools well, measure things carefully, make reasonable estimations, calculate accurately and communicate clearly. And projects also let students ponder the effects their inventions might have.*
- *People, alone or in groups, are always inventing new ways to solve problems and get work done. The tools and ways of doing things that people have invented affect all aspects of life.*
- *Some animals and plants are alike in the way they look and in the things they do, and others are very different from one another. * Plants and animals have features that help them live in different environments.*
- *Stories sometimes give plants and animals attributes they really do not have. Emphasis should be placed on examining a variety of familiar animals and plants and considering things and processes they all need to stay alive, such as food and getting rid of wastes.*
- *Magnifiers help people see things they could not see without them.*
- *Most living things need water, food and air.*

NRC Standard
- *The behavior of individual organisms is influenced by internal cues (such as hunger) and by external cues (such as a change in the environment).*

NCTM Standards 2000*
- *Understand how to measure using nonstandard and standard units*
- *Measure with multiple copies of units of the same size, such as paper clips laid end to end*
- *Use tools to measure*

* Reprinted with permission from *Principles and Standards for School Mathematics*, 2000 by the National Council of Teachers of Mathematics. All rights reserved.

Who Eats What?

Skills
Fractions (fourths)
Time (hours, days)
Animal food
Tools to record (camera)

Materials
Empty pizza boxes (tops removed, ends taped closed)
Assorted bird foods and grit (white bread crumbs, sunflower seeds, cracked feed, corn, egg shells, apple and/or orange slices, raisins, wild bird seed mix)
Poster board strips (2" x 22")
Camera

Directions
1. Have children work in teams of four to construct feeding stations. Each child picks a food to place in his/her section. Have children write their names on the section they have chosen.
2. Place these trays out on the schoolyard where children can observe them. (You may want to use a step ladder so that boxes will be at different heights. Attach so the birds won't tip over the trays.)
3. Children can check trays every hour (good time-telling activity) during school day or at the end of each day for a week. Have them chart which food section was eaten the most. Keep the chart for a week. Have groups compare their results.

Extension
Take a photo each hour of the school day. Identify the birds seen at the time of the photo. Create a time book with picture, clock face with time shown, and text describing what was seen at that time at that particular feeding station.

Playground For the Birds

Skills
Math tools
Measurement
Creating an animal environment

Materials
Paper and pencil
Straight edges (6" and 12" rulers)
Compasses
Protractors
There are several books that show how to make birdhouses. These are two well illustrated books with many attractive photos of birds feeding:
Garden Bird Facts by Marcus Schneck. Barnes and Noble Books. New York. 1992.
How to Attract Birds by Ortho Books (1995).
Use with big book: *A Tree that Grew in the Forest*

Information
   Water sources are as critical as food sources for birds. Encourage children to plan for a waterbath of some sort in their design.

Note
Although these feeders will not actually be constructed out of materials, the process of planning will test the children's knowledge of what birds need to survive. This is especially beneficial for the spatial child. Be sure to make time to listen and scribe or have children write how their design will fit their birds' needs.

Extension
1. Provide 9"x12" pieces of poster board and a collage box of construction paper scraps, glue, and scissors.
2. Demonstrate how to create accordion strips, loops, boxes, etc. from strips of construction paper. Show how to glue one end of the strip to the board and create a three- dimensional stabile piece.
3. Encourage unusual creations of "bird playgrounds." (Pictures from teacher supply catalogs of commercial playgrounds will stimulate ideas—slides, swings, tunnels, etc.)
4. Ask child to describe how birds would use the different apparatus on their "playground." Encourage positional words—over, under, through, next to, etc.

Nests—Science, Mathematics • Activity 2—Teacher Card

Playground For the Birds

Directions
Use a ruler, compass, and protractor or just draw a playground for a bird.

Include:
1. A safe place to build a nest;
2. A place to get food (a feeder or plants with parts a bird might eat—fruit, berries, etc.);
3. A place to get water for drinking and washing.

When you're done, tell your teacher about your playground or tell your story into the tape recorder or write your story down. Be sure to tell why you chose to put in the things you did and how this will help the bird.

Nests • Activity 2—Student Card

This is the Tree That Grew in the Forest

Illustrated by _____.

This is the limb that branched from the tree that grew in the forest

2

This is the tree that grew in the forest.

1

This is the nest that sat on the limb that branched from the tree that grew in the forest.

3

5

This is the baby that hatched from the egg that lay in the nest that sat on the limb that branched from the tree that grew in the forest.

7

This is the mother who scratched for the worm that fed the baby that hatched from the egg that lay in the nest that sat on the limb that branched from the tree that grew in the forest.

4

This is the egg that lay in the nest that sat on the limb that branched from the tree that grew in the forest.

6

This is the worm that fed the baby that hatched from the egg that lay in the nest that sat on the limb that branched from the tree that grew in the forest.

9

LET'S SAVE THAT TREE!

11

8

This is the feather from under the wing of the mother who scratched for the worm that fed the baby that hatched from the egg that lay in the nest that sat on the limb that branched from the tree that grew in the forest.

10

The End

Where Do I Live?

Skills
Creative writing
Habitat

Materials
3" paper squares (1 per child)
9" x12" white paper (2 per child)
1 file folder per child
String
Scissors
Glue
Hole punch

Directions
1. Have children each choose a bird and an environment.
2. Invite each child to draw the bird on the 3" paper square, filling the square and coloring the bird.
3. At the bottom of one of the white papers, have the children copy the frame sentence, "Do you live in a _____?" Children illustrate themselves in that bird's habitat. (i.e., tree—child in tree)
4. At the bottom of the second white paper, the child copies the frame sentence, "No, no. A _____ (baby bird) lives in a _____ (nest). Child does second drawing without self in the picture.
5. Glue the two pages inside the file folder. (First page on left, second page on right.) Make a slit where bird would go in the picture. Punch a hole in the bird square and bottom of right side of file folder. Attach bird to the second page with string. Make sure the string is long enough to put the bird in the tree.

Book Idea—"Where Do I Live?"
Do you live in a nest?
  No, no—a baby bird lives in a nest.
Do you live in a tree?
  No, no—a sparrow lives in a tree.
Do you live in a barn?
  No, no—an owl lives in a barn.
Do you live near a pond?
  No, no—a duck lives near a pond.
Do you live by an ocean?
  No, no—a seagull lives near an ocean.
Do you live in a rainforest?
  No, no—a toucan lives in a rainforest.
Do you live in a desert?
  No, no—a roadrunner lives in the desert.

Lift the Flap

Skills
Music
Creative writing
Habitat

Materials
File folders
Construction paper
Scissors
Glue

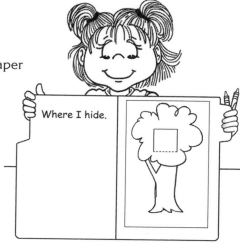

Directions
1. Children will choose a bird and an environment. (See suggestions in *Where Do I Live?* or another of their choosing.)
2. Child draws an environment picture on construction paper and then cuts out a peep hole. On the file folder, the child draws a matching environment picture with the bird in it. (The peep hole needs to reveal a part of the bird, so attach the flap to the right side of the folder before beginning the file folder picture.
3. On the left of the file folder write *Where I hide* and have children write or teacher scribe what the bird's name is, where the habitat is, and how the habitat protects and/or provides for bird.

Nests—Science, Literary Link • Activity 4—Teacher Card

Lift the Flap

Directions

1. On your paper, draw a picture of a place for a bird to live and build a nest. Cut out a "peep hole" from your paper. This will be the flap. Glue the top of your paper to the file folder on side 2.

2. Fold up your glued flap and draw more of the same habitat. Put a bird in your habitat. Be sure we can see one part of the bird when you lower the flap. Hide the rest of the bird under the flap.

3. On the other side of the folder, finish the story: Where I hide. Tell
   a) the bird's name;
   b) where and how it builds its nest; and
   c) how its habitat protects it and provides it with food.

Nests • Activity 4—Student Card

Who Lives Here?

—by Donna VanderWeide

Who lives in the for - est?   Who lives in the for - est?

Lift the flap   Lift the flap   A

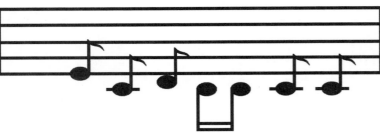

toucan lives in the rain - forest.

Verses:
1. Who lives in Antarctica? Who lives in Antarctica?
   Lift the flap . . . A penguin lives in Antarctica.
2. ...barn? barn owl
3. ...cactus (saguaro)? woodpecker
4. ...oven nest? El hornero
5. ...mountain?
6. an eagle
7. ...water? loon
   (or duck or flamingo)

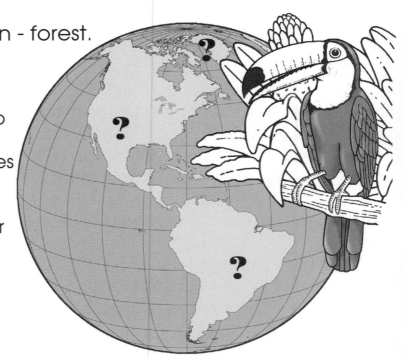

Build a Bird Feeder

Skills
Habitat feeder
Using tools

Materials
Empty milk cartons
Dowels (cut in 1' lengths)
Phillips head screwdriver
Pipe cleaners
Bird seed
Resealable plastic bag
Large nail hammer
1 cup measure
Large thick wood board

Directions
- Pre-cut two round holes in opposite sides of the cartons.
- Children will use screw driver to punch holes through carton **under** the windows. Dowels inserted through these holes will serve as perches.
- Children will take the bird feeders home.

Nests—Science • Activity 5—Teacher Card

Build a Bird Feeder

Directions

1. Use the screwdriver to make perch holes under the windows.
2. Push sticks through the holes.
3. Place carton (top down) on board. (Ask a friend to hold carton.) Use hammer and nail to pound a hole in top.

4. Put pipe cleaner through the hole and twist closed.
5. Put 1 cup of birdseed in a plastic bag. Take bag home and fill feeder with seed.
6. Hang feeder on a tree near a window where you can watch.

Nests • Activity 5—Student Card

String Birds Along

Skills
Habitat feeder
Patterns

Materials
Cheese cubes
Popcorn
Raisins (or other dried fruit)
Peanuts in shells
Fishing line thread and large darning needle **or**
   galvanized wire

Directions
Children will make a patterned feeder.

String Birds Along

Directions
1. Choose three food pieces. Make an A-B-C pattern and put them on your line.
2. Pick three more pieces like your first choice and put them on your line in the same order as your first three pieces.
3. Read your pattern to a friend or teacher.
4. Hang your bird feeder on a branch near a window at your house.
5. Watch: Which food got eaten first? ...second? ...last?

153

Peanut Butter and Corn

Skills
Habitat feeder

Materials
1 cup peanut butter*
5 cups cornmeal
Pine cones
Bread
String
Popsicle sticks

* Peanut butter may choke birds by itself, so mix with cornmeal

Directions
- Tie 12" string around base of cone and leave ends free to tie around tree limb.
- Stuff bread pieces into pinecone and spread peanut butter mixture.
- Roll in bird seed.

Nests—Science, Mathematics • Activity 7—Teacher Card

✂

Peanut Butter and Corn

Directions
1. Break apart bread and stuff in pine cone.
2. Add peanut butter mixture.
3. Roll in bird seed

Nests • Activity 7—Student Card

© 2004 AIMS Education Foundation

Habitat Habitat
(Tune: "Lollipop, Lollipop")
—by Donna VanderWeide

Habitat, habitat - you've got to have a habitat
Habitat, habitat - you've got to have a habitat
Habitat, habitat - you've got to have a habitat
You've got to have a habitat that you can depend on.

You need some food that you can eat.
You need some place that you can sleep.
You need somewhere that you can nest.
You've got to have a habitat that you can depend on.

You need some place where you can drink.
You need some place where you can hide.
You need some place to find a mate.
You've got to have a habitat that you can depend on.

Move it, Chick

Skills
One-to-one correspondence
Subtraction

Materials
9" x12" construction paper
Envelope for storage of birds
Poster board

Directions
1. Cut construction paper so that you have six pieces that are $4\frac{1}{2}$" x 12" pages. Cut poster board in half.
2. Write "**5 Little Chickadees**" on one page. Attach envelope to page.
3. Write each verse on the subsequent pages. Staple together as a book and staple to the cut poster board.
4. Cut 5 "chickadees" from construction paper and place in envelope for storage.
5. Begin story by placing birds in slits. As story is told, remove a bird and place back in envelope.

5 Little Chickadees

5 little chickadees, sitting on a door—
1 flew away, and then there were 4

Refrain:
Chickadee, chickadee—happy and gay.
Chickadee, chickadee—fly, fly away.

4 little chickadees, sitting in a tree—
1 flew away, and then there were 3.
Refrain

3 little chickadees, looking at you—
1 flew away, and then there were 2.
Refrain

2 little chickadees, sitting in the sun—
1 flew away, and then there was 1.
Refrain

1 little chickadee, sitting all alone—
He flew away and then there were none.
Refrain

Nests—Science, Literary Link • Teacher Card

Little Chickadees

Birds Mini-Diary

Skills
Life cycle
Sequence
Ordinal words
Days of the week
Passage of time

Directions
Using a weekly format (i.e., Eric Carle's *A Very Hungry Caterpillar*) child pretends he/she is a mother, father, or baby bird. Child writes about happenings of a week in their life in spring (i.e., *"Monday I could feel my egg begin to move."*). For pre-literate child, teacher could take dictation.

Nests—Science, Mathematics, Literary Link • Teacher Card

Eating Nests

Skills
Measurement
Sequence

Directions
$\frac{1}{2}$ cup melted butter
3 oz. chow mein noodles
1 cup brown sugar

Boil and stir butter and sugar for 1 minute. Stir in noodles. Place in 12 paper muffin cups. Children thumb press into nest shape. Cool. Add jellybeans for eggs.

159

Outdoor Game

Sparrow - Sparrow - Raptor
(Duck-Duck-Goose)

Teacher Information

Some birds share their nests. Some raptors (eagles, hawks, vultures) let sparrows share their larger nesting platforms. The sparrows alert the raptors when predators approach. The raptors, in turn, protect the sparrows.

Directions

Children sit in a circle. One child is the "predator." Child goes around the circle touching each child's head saying - "sparrow" each time. At one child, the toucher will say "raptor." "Raptor" chases "predator" around the circle back to the empty space left by "raptor." If "raptor" catches the "predator," then "predator" has to go again. If "predator" is not caught, he/she stays in the circle and the "raptor" becomes the new "predator."

Spin a Story

Encourage students to create a story with a beginning, middle and ending. Use senses: How does it look, smell, feel, sound, taste? Illustrate. Read to a friend. Ask for suggestions to make it funnier, sadder, more exciting. What should be changed? What should be kept? Decide on many titles. Choose your favorite.

Let students spin the spinners to determine components of their stories. These tend to be very humerous.

Bird
- eagle
- bluebird
- gull
- ostrich
- peacock
- penguin

Setting
- in the woods
- on the water
- in the jungle
- over the grass
- on ice
- in the desert

Action
- no flying / run
- walk slowly
- waddle
- soar
- flutter
- swoop

162

Bird Winners
Station Cards

Children are fascinated with the biggest and the best. This set of activity cards looks at several birds and their unusual statistics.

By using comparison terms (greater than, less than, shorter, taller, bigger, smaller, etc.) numbers take on relevance.

By encouraging teamwork, communication is encouraged.

By using various measuring devices, communication of relative sizes and comparison becomes more exact.

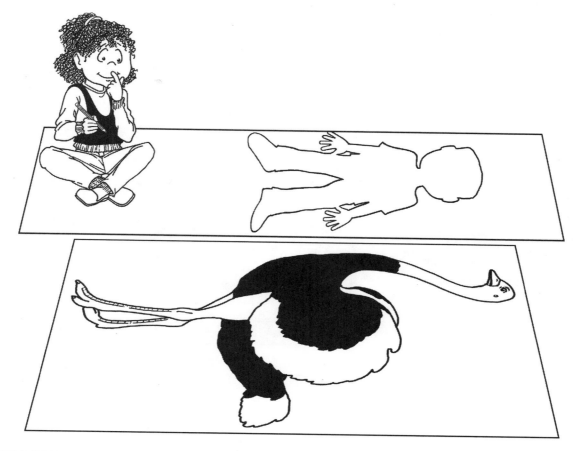

Eagle Eyes

Materials
Binoculars
Journals or paper
Pencils

Background Information
Eagles (and other birds of prey like hawks and owls) have telescopic vision that enables them to see prey easily.

Directions
- Child will choose an item on the playground.
- Child will draw what he or she sees with their eyes.
- Child will use binoculars to look at item and draw what is then seen.

(See AIMS publication *Sense-able Science*, "The Eyes Have It.")

Bird Winners—Senses • Activity 1—Teacher Card

Eagle Eyes

1. Choose an item on the playground.
2. Draw what you see with your eyes.
3. Look at the same item with "Eagle Eyes" (binoculars). Draw what you see.

Bird Winners—Senses • Activity 1—Student Card

Ostrich Eyes

Materials
Old tennis balls (ask tennis club for old practice balls)
Construction paper
Scissors
Glue

Background Information
Ostriches have the biggest eyes of any land animal alive today. They are about the size of a tennis ball. Encourage children to use comparative size words (larger, smaller) when describing the ball and their own eye.

Directions
- Give child a tennis ball.
- Have child add construction paper eyelashes to the tennis ball.
- Ask child to compare the size of tennis ball eye to his or her own eye.

Bird Winners—Senses • Activity 2—Teacher Card

- ✂

Ostrich Eyes

1. Use a tennis ball.
2. Add eyelashes. This is the size of an ostrich's eyeball.
3. How does the size compare to your eyeball? Tell someone about your eyes.

Bird Winners—Senses • Activity 2—Student Card

Tallest Bird

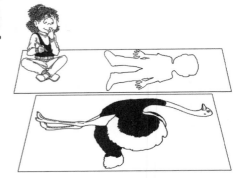

Materials
Adding machine tape
8 1-foot rulers
Scissors
Masking tape
Ostrich picture (drawn on at least 8-foot long sheet of butcher paper), laminate or cover with clear contact paper

Background Information
Ostriches are over 8 feet tall. They are the tallest birds alive today.

Directions
Enlarge ostrich picture from *Heavy Bird* and draw on butcher paper. Tape ostrich picture to floor.

Part One
Children working in pairs will cut a length of adding machine tape that goes from the top of the ostrich to its feet. They will then lay rulers on top of tape to see how many rulers long it is. (It should be **more** than 8 rulers [feet] long.) They can mark off on their tape where each ruler ended. (Remind children rulers have to touch!)

Part Two
Children take turns cutting the tape as along as they are tall. (This can be done with one child laying on the floor next to ostrich **or** child can stand and hold end of tape on top of head and second child cuts off other end of tape on the floor.)

Part Three
Children use rulers (again) to measure themselves and compare to ostrich length.

Extra: Use taller/shorter or < > to write a number sentence about the rulers and their own tapes. Some children may be ready to use terms like, "I am between **3** and **4** rulers tall." Children write their own names on their tapes. (This makes a wonderful wall display, "How do you measure up to an ostrich?")

Bird Winners—Math • Activity 3—Teacher Card

Tallest Bird

Work with a friend:

1. Cut a piece of adding machine tape as long as the ostrich picture.
2. Use the rulers to measure your tape. Lay the rulers on the tape **with their ends touching.** Draw a line across your tape at the **end of each** ruler. How many rulers long was your ostrich tape?
3. Lay down and let your friend cut a piece of adding machine tape as long as your body (top of your head to your feet).
4. Use the rulers and mark off how many rulers tall **you** are. (**Be sure ends of rulers touch!**)

Finish this sentence:
I am _____ rulers tall.
The ostrich is _____ than I am. I am _____ than the ostrich.

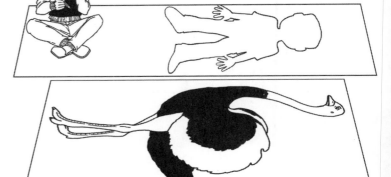

Bird Winners—Math • Activity 3—Student Card

Heavy Bird

Materials

Bathroom scale (digital type will read out actual number)
Journal
Large calculator (the type that works on an overhead is ideal!)
Sticky notes

Background Information

Ostriches can weigh over 345 pounds.

Directions

- Have children weigh themselves and write their results on a sticky note and place it on the chart. At the end of the day, choose three sticky notes. Enter into calculator. How do they compare? Use words **heavier, lighter, weighs more, weighs less**.
- Choose four children's sticky notes. Add and compare. Continue with different combinations. Enter on chart.

Note: Be very sensitive to children who are reluctant to being weighed. Do not use names on the sticky notes.

Bird Winners—Math • Activity 4—Teacher Card

- ✂

Heavy Bird

1. Step on scale.
2. Write your weight on a sticky note.
3. Give the sticky note to your teacher so it can be placed on the class chart.

Bird Winners—Math • Activity 4—Student Card

Biggest Egg

Materials
Egg template (6" long)
Yellow construction paper
Scissors
Pencils
Small jelly beans
Transparent tape
Large sheet of bulletin board paper or butcher paper

Background Information
Ostriches have the largest egg (6" long). Bee hummingbird is 2" long and has smallest egg, one that is about the size of a small jelly bean. Have template cut from cardboard of an egg 6" long. Label "Ostrich Egg."

Directions
- Children will trace the egg shape onto yellow paper and cut it out.
- Tape jelly bean (hummingbird egg) to ostrich paper egg. Have pictures of both birds in center. (David Burnie's book *Birds* has egg pictures.)

Bird Winners—Math • Activity 5—Teacher Card

- ✂

Biggest Egg

1. Trace around ostrich egg.
2. Cut it out.
3. Write "ostrich egg" on your cutout.
4. Tape jelly bean to paper ostrich egg. It is the size of a bee hummingbird's egg.
5. Glue ostrich egg to larger paper.

Finish the following sentence:
The largest egg is _____.
The smallest egg is _____

Bird Winners—Math • Activity 5—Student Card

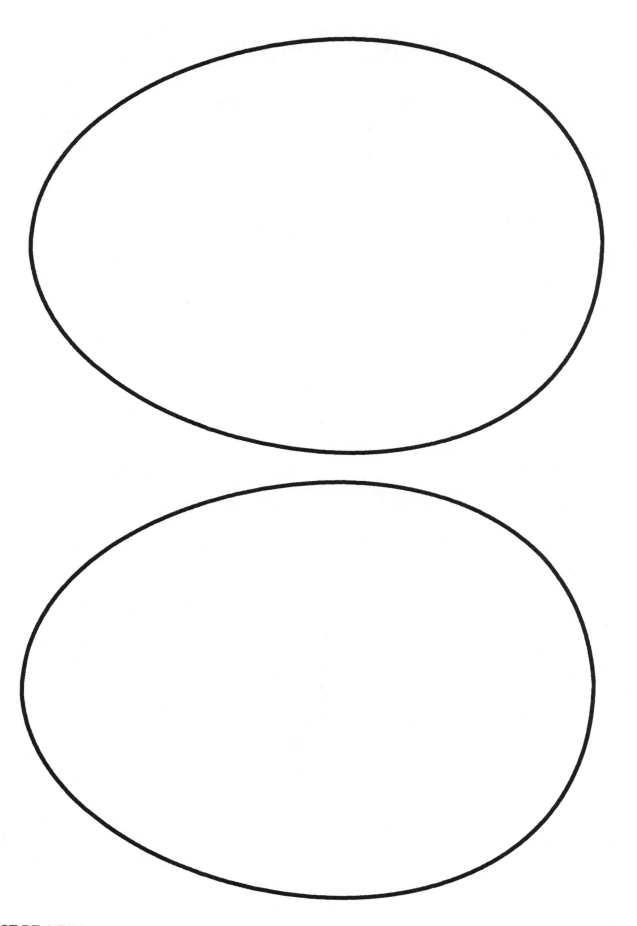

Is Two Enough?

Materials
12-foot length of butcher paper
Scissors
Pencils
Sticky notes
2 Yes/No charts on chart paper
Picture of albatross
2 sentence strips

Background Information
The Wandering Albatross has a wingspan of almost 12 feet.

Preparation
Teacher chart of 12 feet of butcher wrap. (Trim bottom of the butcher paper to resemble feathers.) Mount on wall. Write "Is Two Enough?" on a sentence strip and tape to the wingspan.

Directions
Children will compare their arm spans (fingertip to fingertip with arms spread wide) to the wingspan of the albatross. (It will take about three children to equal the 12-foot span.)

Part One
- Have children form teams of two and stand in front of wings.
- They answer the question: "Is Two Enough?" **Yes** or **No** (Can their two arm spans reach from one end of wingspan to the other?
- Write names of **two** children on sticky note.
- Have them add the sticky note to chart in **yes** or **no** column.

Part Two
- Change label to say "Is Three Enough?" and repeat the exercise with a new **yes/no** chart.

Bird Winners—Math • Activity 6—Teacher Card

Is Two Enough?

Is Two Enough ?

1. Choose a friend to work with.
2. Spread your arms out wide and your friend does the same.

3. Stand with your fingertips touching your friend's and one of your hands at the end of the albatross wing.
4. Does your friend's other hand touch the other end of the albatross wing? Yes_____ No _____
5. Write both your names on a sticky note and place it on the chart.

Bird Winners—Math • Activity 6—Student Card

Culminating Bird Activities

Take a Trip to the Zoo

1. Break into groups (the number of groups will depend on the number of exhibits in your zoo).
2. Assign a parent to each group with an observation checklist.
   - Size
   - Color
   - Feet
   - Beak
   - Zoo Habitat
3. Give each child a clipboard (use stiff cardboard and clothespins), pencil, and drawing paper.
4. Have each group of children visit a different exhibit, make group observations with the parent assigned and then have the children draw their own bird choice. If children can find identifying name tags of the birds, have them copy the names onto their pictures.
5. Reconvene the group and compare findings of each group.
6. Revisiting of four areas. Allow children from "host" area to point out the things they observed.

Take a Walk with the Birds

1. Record bird songs from birds in your area. (Peterson Field Guides has CDs and cassette tapes for *Backyard Bird Song*). **Always** show a picture of the bird as you listen to bird's song. Reread *Feathers for Lunch* by Lois Ehlert for different bird sounds.
2. Read *Good Night, Owl* by Pat Hutchins (Simon & Schuster. New York. 1972).
3. Have children use individual clipboards, paper and pencil to record birds they see and/or hear as you walk around the neighborhood by your school.
4. Optional: Try using an Audubon bird caller on the playground to see if you could make sounds that other birds would respond to!

Extension
Provide xylophones or bells or water jars and have children recreate bird songs **or** write their own bird tunes.

You are a Camera

This is a two-child game. One child stands behind the second child and places both hands on second child's shoulder. The second child is the "camera" and closes his/her eyes. Child One guides Child Two around the classroom (avoiding obstacles by exerting pressure on child's shoulders to stir right/left, slow down, stop, etc.) Child One visits classroom bird displays (i.e. wall murals, bird pictures, feather display at science center). When Child One finds something interesting, he/she stops "the camera" and taps the shoulder of Child Two. Child Two says "CLICK" and opens and closes eyes quickly, then tells Child One what she/he saw. Visit three places and then have children switch rolls.

Move Like a Bird

Play the music to *Swam Lake* and tell students that you will give them some directions so they can "move like a bird."

Soar like an eagle
Bottoms up like a duck
Flightless bird (run fast)
Waddle like a duck
Stretch neck like swan
Hop on both feet
Eat worms with your beak
Fly up and down like hummingbird
Grab things with your toes (hawk)

If Birds Could Talk

Tell a story about your favorite bird. Use the voice and assume the body shape you think that bird would be like. (e.g., *Hawk—large and screeching! Hummingbird—small and fast!*)

Rap

Create a rap to perform for friends (especially good for woodpecker!).

Blue Jay

Falcon

Grosbeak

Heron

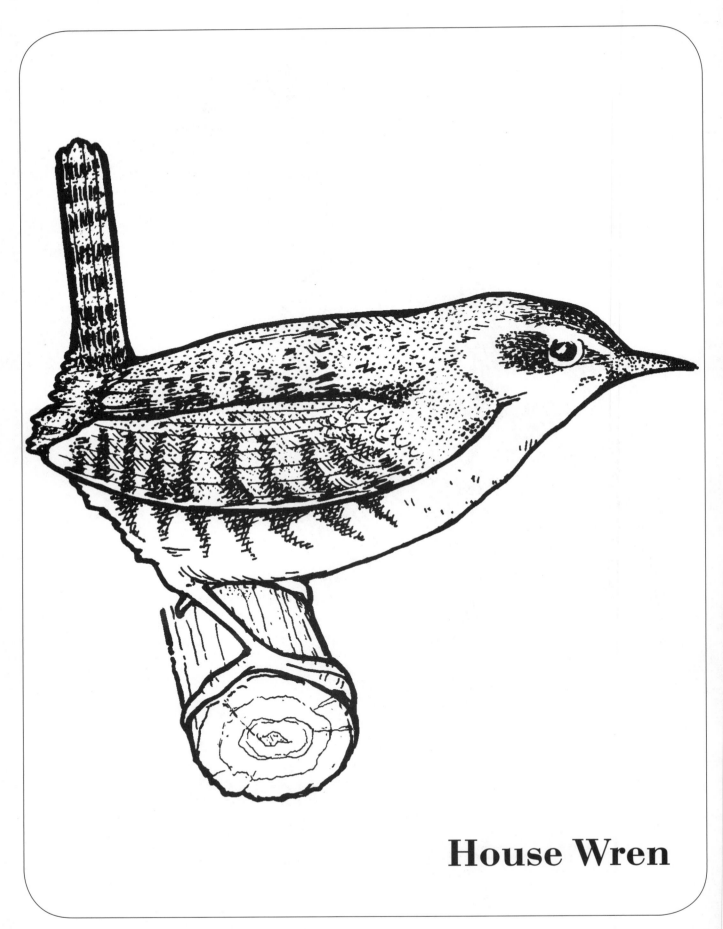

House Wren

Hummingbird

Mourning Dove

Northern Flicker

179

Oriole

Ostrich

Peacock

Pelican

Penguin

Rhea

Snipe

Spoonbill

Swan

Toucan

Warbler

Woodpecker

Blue Jay

Oriole

House Wren

Red-wing Blackbird

Robin

Northern Flicker

Mourning Dove

Goldfinch

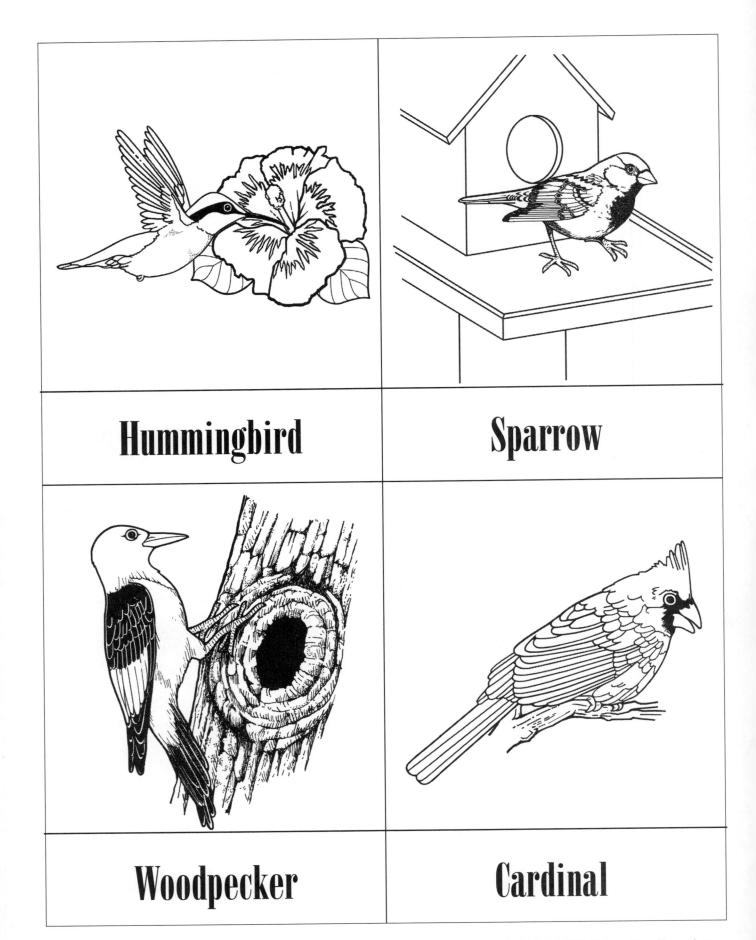

Hummingbird

Sparrow

Woodpecker

Cardinal

Tissue Paper Bird

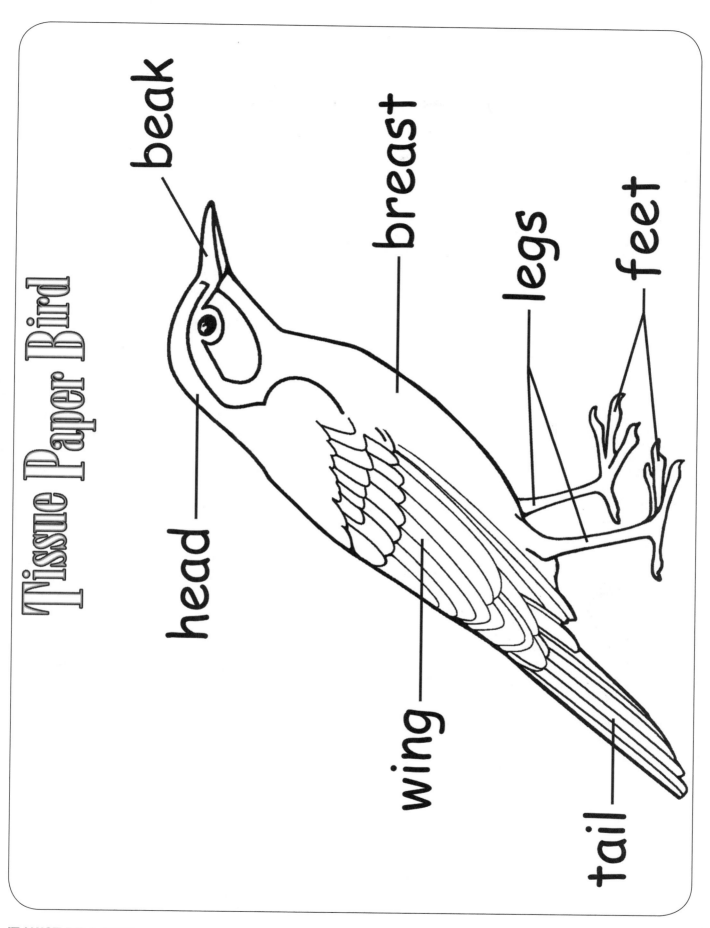

beak

breast

legs

feet

head

wing

tail

Poetry for the Birds

Poetry has many purposes in a primary age classroom. It has a strong emotional base of building community through shared chanting of familiar rhymes. It creates a common bond of gaining the children's attention during transition times. It provides a mnemonic device for remembering important facts and terms while expanding the child's speaking and listening vocabulary. As a literary device, the use of rhyme, meter, and rhythm supports the pre-literacy experiences of the language-rich environment necessary in all academic learning.

The beauty of poetry is that it is enjoyed by all ages and all academic levels. The important re-reading and re-telling of literature pieces are easily accomplished when poetry is written on charts where children can chant and track and re-read words with which they are familiar.

1. Do *Instant Poetry* with whole class. Record on large chart. This does not have to rhyme and it takes three steps to create.
   a. Choose three words for first line (e.g., Birds, fly, high)
   b. Add one word (e.g., Birds, fly, high, overhead)
   c. For third (and following lines) delete the first word of preceding line and add new word to the end of the line.

   > fly, overhead, high, soaring
   > overhead, high, soaring, up
   > high, soaring, up, until
   > down, they, swoop.

   d. Continue the process until the idea for the last line comes into place.

Note: This works well with the whole class providing words in a brainstorming atmosphere. It's always a satisfactory experience and makes for a wonderful chart story to be illustrated by the child.

2. **Two Word Wonder Poetry**
   Use paired words in five or six lines.

   > Bird hop
   > Then fly
   > Eat worms
   > Build nest
   > Lay eggs
   > In trees

3. **Acrostic**
   Use with a specific bird name or as exemplified with the word BIRDS.
   B beautiful beaks
   I into the air (or water)
   R ride the winds (or thermals)
   D dip into water
   S soar into the sky

4. **Numbers of a Bird**
   One is the number of a bird's _____ (beak).
   Two is the number of a bird's _____.
   Three is the eggs in a _____ nest.
   Four is the number of a bird's _____.
   Five is the number of a bird's _____.
   (Illustrate with bird numbers.)

5. Published Poetry

Use these poems in your classroom as you study birds. You'll be amazed how much poetry will add to your children's understanding of science and math.

The Woodpecker, Elizabeth Maddox Roberts
The Little Bird, Old Nursery Rhyme
Egg Thoughts, Russell Hoban
Peck, Peck, Peck, Aileen Fisher
Meg's Egg, Mary Ann Hoberman
April and May, Anonymous
Two Little Blackbirds, Old Nursery Rhyme
The North Wind Doth Blow, Anonymous
The Meal/Knitted Things, Karla Kuskin
Song of the Train, David McCord
Oodles of Noodles, L. & J. L. Hymes, Jr.
Band Aids/Hug O'War/Valentine, Shel Silverstein
Willie Ate A Worm, Jack Prelutsky
Hey, Bug!, Lillie Moore
The People, Elizabeth Maddox Roberts
Mud, Polly Chase Boyden
Grandpa Dropped His Glasses, Leroy E. Jackson

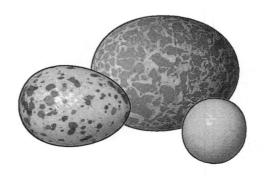

The Random House: Book of Poetry for Children, selected by Jack Prelutsky, illustrated by Arnold Lobel
The Hummingbird
    The Canary
    Duck's Ditty
    The Blackbird
    Sea Gull
    The Sandpiper
    Something Told the Wild Geese
    The Hen
    Night Heron
    The Vulture
    The Eagle
    The Sparrow Hawk
    Egg Thoughts
    Meg's Egg
    The Worm
    The Puffin

Side by Side: Poems to Read Together, collected by Lee Bennett Hopkins
    Wild Geese

Sing a Song of Popcorn, selected by Beatrice Schenk de Regniers
    I Heard a Bird Sing
    Good Morning
    The Duck
    A Bird

Bird Jokes

Humor is a strong indicator of intelligence. Being able to play on words is a wonderful linguistic exercise. Do these for fun and watch which children see the humor and ask to add more of their own. They'll be using vocabulary terms from your unit of study in a very creative way! It allows for that synthesis level of Bloom's Taxonomy.

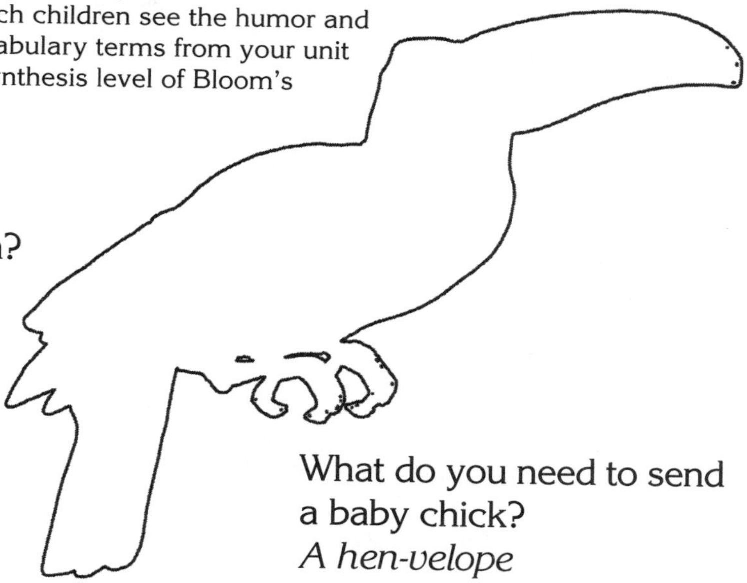

Why does a duck's roof leak in the rain?
Because of all the quacks in the roof!

Knock-knock
Who's there?
Waddle
Waddle who?
Waddle I do if it rains?

What do you need to send a baby chick?
A hen-velope

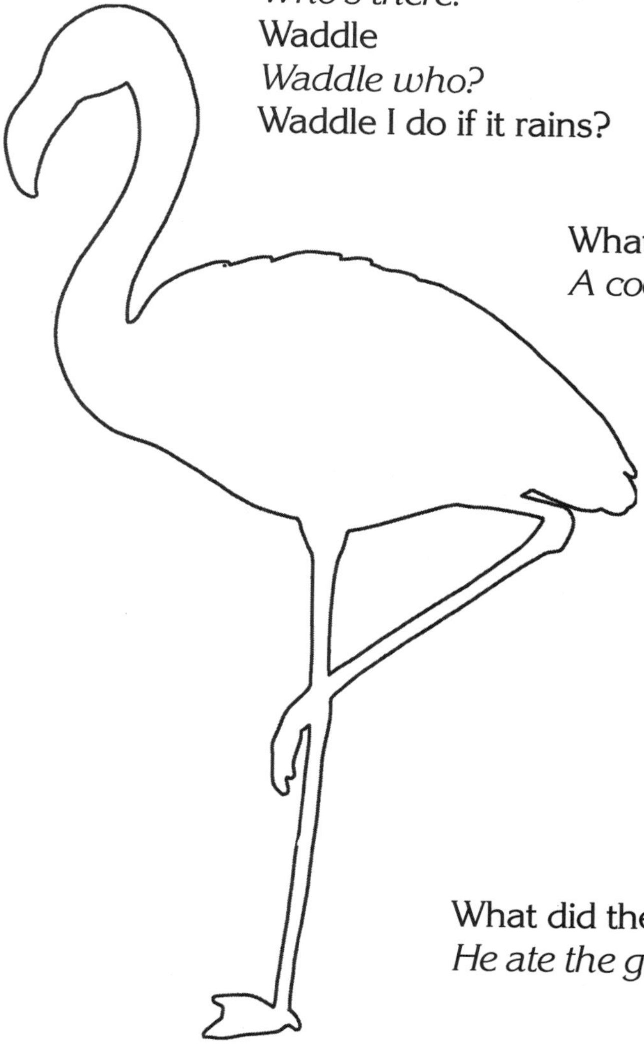

What was the head chef called in the hen house?
A cook-a-doodle-doo!

What song do you sing on a bird's birthday?
Happy "Bird-day" to you!

Why did the robin go to the hospital?
For a tweet-ment!

What did the canary's valentine card say?
Let me call you tweet-heart.

What did the hawk do when he got a birthday present?
He ate the gift—CARDINAL (card and all)

Teacher Resoruce Books

Bird—A Science Activity Book by Pat & Barbara Ward. Mark Twain Publishing Company; Carson/Dellosa Publishers. 1993.

Burnie, David. *Bird*. Alfred A. Knopf (Eyewitness Books). New York. 1988.

Cosgrove, Irene. *My Recipes are For the Birds*. Doubleday Dell Publishing Group, Inc. New York. 1976.

Dennis, John V. and Michael McKinley. *How to Attract Birds*. The Solaris Group. San Ramon, CA. 1995.

Griffin, Steven A. and Elizabeth May. *Birdwatching for Kids*. Northwood Press, Inc. Minocqua, WI. 1995. (800-336-5666).

Klutz Press Editors. *Everybody's Everywhere Backyard Bird Book*. Klutz Press. Palo Alto, CA. 1992. (415) 857-0888 (Comes with Audubon Birdcall).

Peterson, Roger Tory. *Flash Guide: Backyard Books*. Houghton Mifflin Co. New York. 1996. (Has accompanying CD of Backyard Bird Songs)

Ranger Rick's Nature Scope. National Wildlife Federation. Washington, DC.

Rupp, Rebecca. *Everything You Never Learned About Birds*. Pownal, Vermont: Storey Communications, Inc. 1995.

Schneck, Marcus. *Garden Bird Facts*. Barnes and Noble. New York. 1992.

Taylor, Barbara. *Birds*. Dorling Kindersley Book. New York. 1995.

Van Cleave, Janice. *Animals*. John Wiley and Sons, Inc. New York. 1993.

Bibliography

_____ *Birds*. Carson, CA: Educational Insights. 1995.

Bruce, Jill B. *Whose Chick is That?* Kangaroo Press Pty Ltd. Australia. 1995.

Butler, M. Christina. *Too Many Eggs*. David R. Godine Publishers, Inc. Boston. 1988.

de Paola, Tomie. *Watch Out for the Chicken Feet in Your Soup*. Simon and Schuster. New York. 1974.

Duffy, Dee Dee. *Barnyard Tracks*. Boyds Mills Press, Inc. Honesdale, PA. 1992.

Ehlert, Lois. *Feathers for Lunch*. Harcourt Brace Co. New York. 1990.

Jeunesse, Gallimard. *Penguins*. First Discovery Book. Scholastic, Inc. New York. 1995.

Flack, Marjorie. *The Story About Ping*. Scholastic, Inc. New York. 1933.

Fox, Mem. *Hattie and the Fox*. New York: Aladdin Books. New York. 1986.

Gallop, Louise. *Owl's Secret*. Paws IV Publishing. Homer, AK. 1993.

Gans, Roma. *How Do Birds Find Their Way?* Harper Collins Publishers. New York. 1996.

Garland, Sherry. *Why Ducks Sleep on One Leg*. Scholastic, Inc. New York. 1993.

Halperns, Shari (illustrator).). *Little Robin Redbreast (A Mother Goose Rhyme)*. North-South Books, Inc. New York. 1994.

Hawcock, David. *Making Tracks*. Hyperion Books for Children. New York. 1994.

Hutchins, Pat. *Rosie's Walk*. Scholastic, Inc. New York. 1987.

Hutchins, Pat. *Good Night Owl*. Aladdin Books. New York. 1972

Lindbergh, Reeve. *The Day the Goose Got Loose*. Scholastic, Inc. New York. 1990.

Nodset, Joan L. *Who Took the Farmer's Hat?* Scholastic, Inc. New York. 1963.

McCloskey, Robert. *Make Way for Ducklings.* Scholastic, Inc. New York. 1941.

Molleson, Diane. *How Ducklings Grow.* Scholastic, Inc. New York. 1993.

Oppenheim, Joanne and Barbara Reed. *Have You Seen Birds?* Scholastic, Inc. New York. 1986.

Peterson, Katherine. *The Tale of the Mandarin Ducks.* Scholastic, Inc. New York. 1990.

Pragoff, Fiona. *My Feather.* Doubleday Dell Publishing Group, Inc. New York. 1989.

Ross, Tom. *Eggbert (The Slightly Cracked Egg).* G. P. Putnam's Sons. New York. 1994.

Rucki, Ani. *Turkey's Gift to the People.* Scholastic, Inc. New York. 1992.

Tafuri, Nancy. *Have You Seen My Duckling?* Penguin Books, Inc. New York. 1986.

Waddell, Martin. *Owl Babies.* Candlewick Press. Cambridge, MA. 1992.

Williams, Sue. *I Went Walking.* Trumpet Club. New York. 1989.

Wolkstein, Diane. *The Magic Wings.* E.P. Dutton. New York. 1983.

Yolen, Jane. *Owl Moon.* Scholastic, Inc. New York. 1987.

Yoshima, Taro. *Crow Boy.* Scholastic, Inc. New York. 1965.

Resoruces

Hawks, Owls & Wildlife
R.D. 1, Box 293
Buskirk, NY 102028
(518) 686-4080
Owl Pellet Mini Kit - $9.50
Bird Chart Set (20" x 29"), set of 4 - $14.00
Audubon Bird Call - $5.00

Teacher Resource Center
P.O. Box 1509
San Leandro, CA 94577
(800) 833-3389
Feathers (for sorting and classifying) - $4.95

Insect Lore
P.O. Box 1535
Shafter, CA 93263
(800) LIVE-BUG
Life Cycle Sequence Cards (frog, butterfly grasshopper, robin,) - $11.95
Eyewitness Bird Video - 12.95
Chicken/Egg - 17.95
Bird Poster (20/ x30/) - $3.95
If You Were A Bird - $6.95
Inside an Egg - $5.95

Additional Resources Used

Andrew, Moira. *Words with Wings.* Belair Publisher, Ltd. Twickenham, England. 1991.

Bredekamp, Sue and Teresa Rosegrant (editors). *Reaching Potentials: Appropriate Curriculum and Assessment for Young Children, Vol. I.* National Association for the Education of Young Children. Washington, DC. 1992.

Charlesworth, Rosalind and Karen K. Lind. *Math and Science for Young Children.* Delmark Publishers. Albany, NY. 1995.

Graves, Donald. *Explore Poetry.* Heinemann. Portsmouth, NH. 1992.

McCracken, Robert and Marlene. Stories, Songs and Poetry to Teach Reading and Writing: Literacy Through Language. Peguis Pub. Ltd. Canada. 1986.

Periodicals

Young Children (Journal of NAEYC)
"Children and the Earth," 48(3), 58-63.
"Science Is a Way of Life," 47(4), 4-8.
"Teachers and Science," 47(4), 9-16.
"Joyful Voices: Facilitating Language Growth through the Rhythmic Response to Chants," 49(4).
"How and Why to Teach all Aspects of Pre-school and Kindergarten Math Naturally, Democratically and Effectively (For Teachers Who Don't Believe in Academic Programs, Who Do Believe in Academic Programs, Who Do Believe in Educational Excellence, and Who Find Math Boring to the Max)—Part 1," 48(4), 75-84.
"How Kids Learn," (Reprint of *Newsweek* Article) 44(6), 6-10.
"Boosting Your Science and Math Programs in Early Childhood Education: Making the Home School Connection," 50(5), 35-39.

Dimensions (Southern Early Childhood Association)
"How Do Caterpillars Make Cocoons?" 22(3), 5-9.
"Go Fishing To Teach Respect for Nature," 18(3), 8-9,32.

Teaching Children Mathematics
"Cooking Up Mathematics in Kindergarten," 2(8), 492-495.
"Adding Taste to Mathematics," 2(4), 224-225.
"Developing Power in Linear Measurement," 1(7), 412-416.
"Take the Magic Out of Your Classroom!" 2(3), 150-153.
"Paper to Pop-up Books," 1(1), 14-17.

Arithmetic Teacher
"Writing-Mathematics Connection!" 40(4), 207-209.
"Thematic Webbing and the Curriculum Standards in the Primary Grades." 41(6), 294-298.

Science and Children
"Put Science in a Bag," 32(4), 19-22.
"An Indoor Study of the Great Outdoors," 29(7), 18-19.
"Bag it for Science," 29(6), 15-16.
"Hands-on, Brains-on," 30(5), 15-16.
"Measure Up to Science," 31(5), 30-31.
"School Yard Spies," 29(1), 34-35.
"A Trip to the Zoo," 32(8), 37.
"Animal Care, Day by Day," 32(1), 30-33.
"How Can We Best Use Children's Literature in Teaching Science Concepts," 32(6), 16-19, 43.
"Science—It's for the Birds," 33(3), 16-19.

The AIMS Program

AIMS is the acronym for "**A**ctivities **I**ntegrating **M**athematics and **S**cience." Such integration enriches learning and makes it meaningful and holistic. AIMS began as a project of Fresno Pacific University to integrate the study of mathematics and science in grades K-9, but has since expanded to include language arts, social studies, and other disciplines.

AIMS is a continuing program of the non-profit AIMS Education Foundation. It had its inception in a National Science Foundation funded program whose purpose was to explore the effectiveness of integrating mathematics and science. The project directors in cooperation with 80 elementary classroom teachers devoted two years to a thorough field-testing of the results and implications of integration.

The approach met with such positive results that the decision was made to launch a program to create instructional materials incorporating this concept. Despite the fact that thoughtful educators have long recommended an integrative approach, very little appropriate material was available in 1981 when the project began. A series of writing projects have ensued and today the AIMS Education Foundation is committed to continue the creation of new integrated activities on a permanent basis.

The AIMS program is funded through the sale of this developing series of books and proceeds from the Foundation's endowment. All net income from program and products flows into a trust fund administered by the AIMS Education Foundation. Use of these funds is restricted to support of research, development, and publication of new materials. Writers donate all their rights to the Foundation to support its on-going program. No royalties are paid to the writers.

The rationale for integration lies in the fact that science, mathematics, language arts, social studies, etc., are integrally interwoven in the real world from which it follows that they should be similarly treated in the classroom where we are preparing students to live in that world. Teachers who use the AIMS program give enthusiastic endorsement to the effectiveness of this approach.

Science encompasses the art of questioning, investigating, hypothesizing, discovering, and communicating. Mathematics is a language that provides clarity, objectivity, and understanding. The language arts provide us powerful tools of communication. Many of the major contemporary societal issues stem from advancements in science and must be studied in the context of the social sciences. Therefore, it is timely that all of us take seriously a more holistic mode of educating our students. This goal motivates all who are associated with the AIMS Program. We invite you to join us in this effort.

Meaningful integration of knowledge is a major recommendation coming from the nation's professional science and mathematics associations. The American Association for the Advancement of Science in *Science for All Americans* strongly recommends the integration of mathematics, science, and technology. The National Council of Teachers of Mathematics places strong emphasis on applications of mathematics such as are found in science investigations. AIMS is fully aligned with these recommendations.

Extensive field testing of AIMS investigations confirms these beneficial results.

1. Mathematics becomes more meaningful, hence more useful, when it is applied to situations that interest students.
2. The extent to which science is studied and understood is increased, with a significant economy of time, when mathematics and science are integrated.
3. There is improved quality of learning and retention, supporting the thesis that learning which is meaningful and relevant is more effective.
4. Motivation and involvement are increased dramatically as students investigate real-world situations and participate actively in the process.

We invite you to become part of this classroom teacher movement by using an integrated approach to learning and sharing any suggestions you may have. The AIMS Program welcomes you!

AIMS Education Foundation Programs

A Day with AIMS®

Intensive one-day workshops are offered to introduce educators to the philosophy and rationale of AIMS. Participants will discuss the methodology of AIMS and the strategies by which AIMS principles may be incorporated into curriculum. Each participant will take part in a variety of hands-on AIMS investigations to gain an understanding of such aspects as the scientific/mathematical content, classroom management, and connections with other curricular areas. *A Day with AIMS®* workshops may be offered anywhere in the United States. Necessary supplies and take-home materials are usually included in the enrollment fee.

A Week with AIMS®

Throughout the nation, AIMS offers many one-week workshops each year, usually in the summer. Each workshop lasts five days and includes at least 30 hours of AIMS hands-on instruction. Participants are grouped according to the grade level(s) in which they are interested. Instructors are members of the AIMS Instructional Leadership Network. Supplies for the activities and a generous supply of take-home materials are included in the enrollment fee. Sites are selected on the basis of applications submitted by educational organizations. If chosen to host a workshop, the host agency agrees to provide specified facilities and cooperate in the promotion of the workshop. The AIMS Education Foundation supplies workshop materials as well as the travel, housing, and meals for instructors.

AIMS One-Week Perspectives Workshops

Each summer, Fresno Pacific University offers AIMS one-week workshops on its campus in Fresno, California. AIMS Program Directors and highly qualified members of the AIMS National Leadership Network serve as instructors.

The AIMS Instructional Leadership Program

This is an AIMS staff-development program seeking to prepare facilitators for leadership roles in science/math education in their home districts or regions. Upon successful completion of the program, trained facilitators may become members of the AIMS Instructional Leadership Network, qualified to conduct AIMS workshops, teach AIMS in-service courses for college credit, and serve as AIMS consultants. Intensive training is provided in mathematics, science, process and thinking skills, workshop management, and other relevant topics.

College Credit and Grants

Those who participate in workshops may often qualify for college credit. If the workshop takes place on the campus of Fresno Pacific University, that institution may grant appropriate credit. If the workshop takes place off-campus, arrangements can sometimes be made for credit to be granted by another institution. In addition, the applicant's home school district is often willing to grant in-service or professional-development credit. Many educators who participate in AIMS workshops are recipients of various types of educational grants, either local or national. Nationally known foundations and funding agencies have long recognized the value of AIMS mathematics and science workshops to educators. The AIMS Education Foundation encourages educators interested in attending or hosting workshops to explore the possibilities suggested above. Although the Foundation strongly supports such interest, it reminds applicants that they have the primary responsibility for fulfilling *current* requirements.

For current information regarding the programs described above, please complete the following:

Information Request

Please send current information on the items checked:

_____ *Basic Information Packet* on AIMS materials
_____ *AIMS Instructional Leadership Program*
_____ *AIMS One-Week Perspectives* workshops

_____ *A Week with AIMS®* workshops
_____ Hosting information for *A Day with AIMS®* workshops
_____ Hosting information for *A Week with AIMS®* workshops

Name _____ Phone _____

Address _____
Street   City   State   Zip

We invite you to subscribe to *AIMS*®!

Each issue of *AIMS*® contains a variety of material useful to educators at all grade levels. Feature articles of lasting value deal with topics such as mathematical or science concepts, curriculum, assessment, the teaching of process skills, and historical background. Several of the latest AIMS math/science investigations are always included, along with their reproducible activity sheets. As needs direct and space allows, various issues contain news of current developments, such as workshop schedules, activities of the AIMS Instructional Leadership Network, and announcements of upcoming publications.

AIMS® is published monthly, August through May. Subscriptions are on an annual basis only. A subscription entered at any time will begin with the next issue, but will also include the previous issues of that volume. Readers have preferred this arrangement because articles and activities within an annual volume are often interrelated.

Please note that an *AIMS*® subscription automatically includes duplication rights for one school site for all issues included in the subscription. Many schools build cost-effective library resources with their subscriptions.

YES! I am interested in subscribing to *AIMS*®.

Name _____   Home Phone _____

Address _____   City, State, Zip _____

Please send the following volumes (subject to availability):

_____Volume	VIII	(1993-94)	$10.00	_____Volume	XIII	(1998-99)	$35.00

_____Volume VIII   (1993-94) $10.00   _____Volume XIII   (1998-99) $35.00
_____Volume IX   (1994-95) $10.00   _____Volume XIV   (1999-00) $35.00
_____Volume X   (1995-96) $10.00   _____Volume XV   (2000-01) $35.00
_____Volume XI   (1996-97) $10.00   _____Volume XVI   (2001-02) $35.00
_____Volume XII   (1997-98) $10.00   _____Volume XVII (2002-03) $35.00
_____**Limited offer: Volumes XVII & XVIII (2002-2004) $60.00**
(Note: Prices may change without notice)

Check your method of payment:

❏ Check enclosed in the amount of $ _____

❏ Purchase order attached (Please include the P.O.#, the authorizing signature, and position of the authorizing person.)

❏ Credit Card   ❏ Visa   ❏ MasterCard   Amount $ _____
Card # _____   Expiration Date _____
Signature _____   Today's Date _____

Make checks payable to **AIMS Education Foundation**.
Mail to *AIMS*® Magazine, P.O. Box 8120, Fresno, CA 93747-8120.
Phone (559) 255-4094 or (888) 733-2467   FAX (559) 255-6396
AIMS Homepage: http://www.AIMSedu.org/

AIMS Program Publications

Actions with Fractions 4-9
Awesome Addition and Super Subtraction 2-3
Bats Incredible! 2-4
Brick Layers 4-9
Brick Layers II 4-9
Chemistry Matters 4-7
Counting on Coins K-2
Cycles of Knowing and Growing 1-3
Crazy about Cotton Book 3-7
Critters K-6
Down to Earth 5-9
Electrical Connections 4-9
Exploring Environments Book K-6
Fabulous Fractions 3-6
Fall into Math and Science K-1
Field Detectives 3-6
Finding Your Bearings 4-9
Floaters and Sinkers 5-9
From Head to Toe 5-9
Fun with Foods 5-9
Glide into Winter with Math & Science K-1
Gravity Rules! Activity Book 5-12
Hardhatting in a Geo-World 3-5
It's About Time K-2
Jaw Breakers and Heart Thumpers 3-5
Just for the Fun of It! 4-9
Looking at Geometry 6-9
Looking at Lines 6-9
Machine Shop 5-9
Magnificent Microworld Adventures 5-9
Marvelous Multiplication and Dazzling Division 4-5
Math + Science, A Solution 5-9
Mostly Magnets 2-8
Movie Math Mania 6-9
Multiplication the Algebra Way 4-8
Off The Wall Science 3-9
Our Wonderful World 5-9
Out of This World 4-8
Overhead and Underfoot 3-5
Paper Square Geometry:
    The Mathematics of Origami
Puzzle Play: 4-8
Pieces and Patterns 5-9
Popping With Power 3-5

Primarily Bears K-6
Primarily Earth K-3
Primarily Physics K-3
Primarily Plants K-3
Proportional Reasoning 6-9
Ray's Reflections 4-8
Sense-Able Science K-1
Soap Films and Bubbles 4-9
Spatial Visualization 4-9
Spills and Ripples 5-12
Spring into Math and Science K-1
The Amazing Circle 4-9
The Budding Botanist 3-6
The Sky's the Limit 5-9
Through the Eyes of the Explorers 5-9
Under Construction K-2
Water Precious Water 2-6
Weather Sense:
    Temperature, Air Pressure, and Wind 4-5
Weather Sense: Moisture 4-5
Winter Wonders K-2

Spanish/English Editions*
Brinca de alegria hacia la Primavera con las
    Matemáticas y Ciencias K-1
Cáete de gusto hacia el Otoño con las
    Matemáticas y Ciencias K-1
Conexiones Eléctricas 4-9
El Botanista Principiante 3-6
Los Cinco Sentidos K-1
Ositos Nada Más K-6
Patine al Invierno con Matemáticas y Ciencias K-1
Piezas y Diseños 5-9
Primariamente Física K-3
Primariamente Plantas K-3
Principalmente Imanes 2-8

* All Spanish/English Editions include student pages in Spanish and
    teacher and student pages in English.

Spanish Edition
Constructores II: Ingeniería Creativa Con Construcciones LEGO® (4-9)
    The entire book is written in Spanish. English pages not included.

Other Science and Math Publications
Historical Connections in Mathematics, Vol. I 5-9
Historical Connections in Mathematics, Vol. II 5-9
Historical Connections in Mathematics, Vol. III 5-9
Mathematicians are People, Too
Mathematicians are People, Too, Vol. II
Teaching Science with Everyday Things
What's Next, Volume 1, 4-12
What's Next, Volume 2, 4-12
What's Next, Volume 3, 4-12

For further information write to:
AIMS Education Foundation • P.O. Box 8120 • Fresno, California 93747-8120
www.AIMSedu.org/ • Fax 559•255•6396

AIMS Duplication Rights Program

AIMS has received many requests from school districts for the purchase of unlimited duplication rights to AIMS materials. In response, the AIMS Education Foundation has formulated the program outlined below. There is a built-in flexibility which, we trust, will provide for those who use AIMS materials extensively to purchase such rights for either individual activities or entire books.

It is the goal of the AIMS Education Foundation to make its materials and programs available at reasonable cost. All income from the sale of publications and duplication rights is used to support AIMS programs; hence, strict adherence to regulations governing duplication is essential. Duplication of AIMS materials beyond limits set by copyright laws and those specified below is strictly forbidden.

Limited Duplication Rights

Any purchaser of an AIMS book may make up to *200 copies* of any activity in that book for use at *one school site*. Beyond that, rights must be purchased according to the appropriate category.

Unlimited Duplication Rights for Single Activities

An individual or school may purchase the right to make an unlimited number of copies of a single activity. The royalty is $5.00 per activity per school site.

Examples: 3 activities x 1 site x $5.00 = $15.00
9 activities x 3 sites x $5.00 = $135.00

Unlimited Duplication Rights for Entire Books

A school or district may purchase the right to make an unlimited number of copies of a single, *specified* book. The royalty is $20.00 per book per school site. This is in addition to the cost of the book.

Examples: 5 books x 1 site x $20.00 = $100.00
12 books x 10 sites x $20.00 = $2400.00

Magazine/Newsletter Duplication Rights

Those who purchase *AIMS*® (magazine)/*Newsletter* are hereby granted permission to make up to 200 copies of any portion of it, provided these copies will be used for educational purposes.

Workshop Instructors' Duplication Rights

Workshop instructors may distribute to registered workshop participants a maximum of 100 copies of any article and/or 100 copies of no more than eight activities, provided these six conditions are met:

1. Since all AIMS activities are based upon the *AIMS Model of Mathematics* and the *AIMS Model of Learning*, leaders must include in their presentations an explanation of these two models.
2. Workshop instructors must relate the AIMS activities presented to these basic explanations of the AIMS philosophy of education.
3. The copyright notice must appear on all materials distributed.
4. Instructors must provide information enabling participants to order books and magazines from the Foundation.
5. Instructors must inform participants of their limited duplication rights as outlined below.
6. Only student pages may be duplicated.

Written permission must be obtained for duplication beyond the limits listed above. Additional royalty payments may be required.

Workshop Participants' Rights

Those enrolled in workshops in which AIMS student activity sheets are distributed may duplicate a maximum of 35 copies or enough to use the lessons one time with one class, whichever is less. Beyond that, rights must be purchased according to the appropriate category.

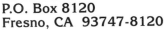